Edward Alden and **Mike Sayer**

Series Adviser **Catherine Walter**

Audio CD included

Navigate

Workbook

with key

B1+ **Intermediate**

OXFORD

UNIVERSITY PRESS

Contents

Oxford 3000™ *Navigate* has been based on the Oxford 3000 to ensure that learners are only covering the most relevant vocabulary.

Vocabulary friendship

4a Match questions 1–6 to answers a–f.

1 Do you get on well with your neighbours?
2 Do you have a lot in common with your partner?
3 When was the last time you had an argument with your best friend?
4 How often do you meet up with your friends?
5 Do you make new friends easily?
6 How many old classmates do you keep in touch with?

a Yesterday! But it was about something stupid, and we've already forgotten about it.
b Maybe four or five, but just on Facebook.
c Not really. I don't even know their names!
d Usually once a week, on Fridays.
e Yes, I'm very sociable. People think I'm crazy because I talk to everyone on the bus!
f Yeah, we like the same music, books and lots of other things.

b **1.1**))) Listen and check.

5 Put the word in brackets in the correct place in each sentence.
1 I fell ^out with my partner once because of football. (out)
2 My parents helped me when I didn't have enough money. (out)
3 I get well with everybody from work. (on)
4 I'm terrible at getting touch with distant relatives. (in)
5 I met up people from work to celebrate a birthday last week. (with)

6 Complete the opinions on social networking with verbs from the box.

have   help   ~~keep~~   make   trust

1 Social networking is great to _keep_ in touch with people who live far away.
2 When I have a problem with my English homework, I can always find someone online to _____ me out.
3 I never _____ people I meet on social networking sites; it's too dangerous.
4 I like joining online groups because you can meet people you _____ a lot in common with.
5 Social networking is a great opportunity to _____ friends with people all over the planet.

➡ **STUDY TIP** Record new words and phrases in your vocabulary notebook under topic headings like *Friendship*. Use them to write true sentences about your friendships.

PRONUNCIATION linking

7a **1.2**))) Listen and repeat.

get‿on   I get on well with her.
met‿up   I met up with my mates yesterday.

b Choose the correct options to complete the rule.

These words are linked (pronounced as one word) because the first word ends with a ¹ *consonant / vowel* sound and the second word starts with a ² *consonant / vowel* sound.

c **1.3**))) Listen and link the words. The number of links is given in brackets next to the sentences.

1 I make‿an‿effort to get‿in touch with distant relatives. (3)
2 I have a lot in common with all my classmates. (3)
3 Could you help Adam out? (2)
4 I keep in touch with old friends. (2)
5 I had an argument with an assistant. (4)
6 It's a shame you fell out with Alice. (3)

d **1.3**))) Listen again. Pause the listening and repeat after each sentence.

I can ...	Very well	Quite well	More practice
talk about things that are changing.	○	○	○
talk about friendships.	○	○	○

Why spending's #trending

Vocabulary spending

1 Match special offers 1–4 to types of shops a–d.

> **1**
> ❄ **Half-price** ❄
> on all frozen meals range
> *limit of 5 identical **items** per **customer**

> **2**
> **Two for the price of one**
> on all titles with yellow stickers

> **3**
> Great meal **deals**
> for families
> See separate menu

> **4**
> **40% discount**
> on men's and children's wear

a Book shop ___   c Supermarket _1_
b Clothes shop ___   d Restaurant ___

2 Match the words in bold in exercise **1** to the definitions.

1 products   _items_
2 a reduction in the price   _____
3 you pay for one item and
   receive two of the same   _____
4 a person who buys
   products or services   _____
5 you pay 50% of the
   original price   _____
6 special negotiations in
   certain conditions   _____

3 Read the text about shopping holidays and choose the best options to complete the text.

1 a (discount)   b shopping   c consumer
2 a shopping   b offer   c shopper
3 a special offer b deal   c item
4 a purchases   b customers   c discounts
5 a half-price   b purchases   c special offers
6 a half-price   b bargains   c consumers
7 a Deals   b Items   c Shoppers
8 a half-price   b bargain   c offer
9 a offers   b consumers   c purchases

Shopping Holidays

People usually travel for different reasons: to relax, to visit historical places or to get a suntan. But more and more people now travel the world looking for a good ¹_a_ ! Here are some top ²___ destinations around the world:

Hong Kong It's considered the best place in East Asia to make a good ³___, but be careful with the shop assistants, who can persuade even the most experienced ⁴___ to buy something they don't really want or need!

Madrid You can find ⁵___ in more than 50,000 shops around town, but don't miss *El Rastro*, an enormous street market with lots of amazing ⁶___.

Mexico ⁷___ from around the world come here to buy very cheap, but high-quality, hand-made goods.

Bangkok The secret of its huge outdoor markets is to bargain with the sellers. Never accept the first price and you can even get a product ⁸___!

One last tip: Just make sure you have room for all your ⁹___ in your luggage!

Grammar state verbs

4 Complete the sentences with the correct form of the verbs in the box.

~~believe~~ own seem taste understand

1 I _believe_ we buy far more than we really need.
2 My family has _____ this business for over thirty years.
3 This pasta _____ fantastic! You must give me the recipe.
4 I don't know him very well, but he _____ very friendly.
5 I really don't _____ why people need to buy a new mobile phone when their old one works fine.

5 Choose the correct form of the verbs to complete the sentences.

1 I (want)/ 'm wanting to buy a new laptop.
2 I know / 'm knowing a lot about economics.
3 I spend / 'm spending a lot of money eating in restaurants at the moment because I haven't got time to cook.
4 I have / 'm having a really hard time with this maths exercise. Can you help me?
5 I never buy / 'm never buying things on impulse. I always make a shopping list and only buy what's on it.
6 I see / 'm seeing a lot of shops on my way to work.

6 Are these sentences always true (A) or are they only true now (N)?

1 a Freshly cut grass smells great! _A_
   b I smell smoke. Did you turn off the oven? _N_
2 a I don't understand much about chemistry. ___
   b I don't understand what you're saying. ___
3 a I love this jacket! You should definitely buy it. ___
   b I love autumn – it's wonderful. ___
4 a What do you mean by 'we have a problem'? ___
   b What does this word mean? ___
5 a I have a cousin who looks like Rafael Nadal. ___
   b You look exhausted. Bad day at work? ___

7 Read this leaflet about compulsive buying. Find and correct four more mistakes related to state verbs.

Are you a shopaholic?

1 The number of shopaholics is increasing all over the world. Psychologists now ~~are understanding~~ *understand* the reasons for this behaviour better, and have identified seven important signs:

5 • You're always buying items you aren't needing.

   • You don't unpack your purchases but keep them in their boxes with the price tag on.

   • You're wanting to go shopping every day and feel anxious if you don't.

10 • You're hiding your shopping from family and friends.

   • You feel excited when you're shopping.

   • You feel bad the next day because you're knowing you shouldn't go shopping all the

15 time.

   • An argument or disappointment makes you want to shop.

What to do

If these sentences are seeming true for you, you might be a compulsive shopper. There
20 are lots of things you can do to shop less: find a new activity, stop going to shopping centres, and don't carry credit cards when you go out – only a little cash. You can also receive help from your local support group.

I can ...	Very well	Quite well	More practice
talk about spending.	○	○	○
talk about states, thoughts and feelings.	○	○	○

1.3 Vocabulary development

Vocabulary noun suffixes

1 Add suffixes to the words in the box to form nouns.

> able achieve communicate friend govern inform
> member secure

1 -ity: _ability_ , _____
2 -tion: _____ , _____
3 -ment: _____ , _____
4 -ship: _____ , _____

2 Choose the correct nouns from exercise **1** to complete the sentences below.

1 Do you think the _government_ should control what goes on the internet?
2 Companies are always improving online _____ to protect their data.
3 It is estimated that the internet has more than five million terabytes of _____ .
4 I'm impressed by his _____ to navigate the Web and get the best out of it.
5 The Web is a good place to start a _____ , but you have to be careful with personal information.

3 Read the text and complete it using the words in the correct form.

Children and the internet

Although parents are usually worried about the negative effects of the internet on their children, there is new ¹ _information_ from recent research that might change their minds. — **INFORM**

Scientists have proved that internet use can lead to ² _____ in memory, concentration and critical thinking. It also helps with children's ³ _____ to solve problems. — **IMPROVE** / **ABLE**

There has been considerable ⁴ _____ in terms of language skills, and research has also shown that the internet can stimulate children's ⁵ _____ . — **DEVELOP** / **IMAGINE**

They can even use the Web to form ⁶ _____ with other children, although online ⁷ _____ have to be monitored by parents. — **RELATION** / **FRIEND**

PRONUNCIATION word stress

4a Mark the stress pattern (the number of syllables and main stress) as in the examples.

1 membership — _Ooo_
2 judgement — _Oo_
3 solution — _____
4 celebrity — _____
5 employment — _____
6 information — _____
7 friendship — _____

b **1.4**))) Listen and check. Then listen again, pause after each word and repeat.

Vocabulary review

5a Complete the phrases with the words in the box.

> have help in keep make on ~~out~~ touch up

Friendships

fall ¹ _out_ (with someone)
get in ² _____ (with someone)
get ³ _____ well (with someone)
have a lot ⁴ _____ common (with someone)
⁵ _____ an argument (with someone)
⁶ _____ someone out
⁷ _____ in touch (with someone)
⁸ _____ friends (with someone)
meet ⁹ _____ with someone

b Complete the words with the missing vowels.

Spending

1 b__rg____ns
2 d____ls
3 h__lf-pr__ce
4 sp__c____l
  __ff__rs
5 tw__ f__r th__
  pr__c__ __f __ne
6 d__sc____nts
7 __t__ms
8 p__rch__s__s
9 sh__p____ng
10 sh__p____rs
11 c__st__m__rs
12 c__ns____rs

1.4   Speaking and writing

Speaking   asking for and giving opinions

1a **1.5))** Listen to five people talking about the internet. Are their opinions positive (P) or negative (N)?

1 _P_ 2 ___ 3 ___ 4 ___ 5 ___

b **1.5))** Complete the sentences with one word. Then listen again and check.

a How do you _feel_ about the internet?

b Well, _____ people say that the internet ...

c ... but _____ , I think that it's an essential ...

d It's a terrible thing, if you ask _____ .

e Don't you _____ they're just wasting their lives?

f I'm _____ that everybody's gone mad ...

g I _____ think that life is much better ...

h ... but as _____ as I'm concerned, it's got ...

2 Correct the mistakes in sentences 1–5.

1 ~~So~~ far as I'm concerned, the government should invest more in preventing crime than fighting it.
   As

2 I think definitely that TV programmes are getting worse.

3 How do you think about carbon taxes?

4 According my wife, football should be banned!

5 I'm really feel that higher education should be free.

3 **1.6))** Complete the conversation between Marion (M) and her husband (H), daughter (D) and son (S). Then listen and check.

> **M** So, ¹ _how_ do you feel ² _____ moving from Sydney to a smaller city?
>
> **H** It's a great idea, if ³ _____ ask ⁴ _____ . This is the most expensive city in Australia, according ⁵ _____ this article I've just read in the paper. Houses are the most expensive in the country, and we hardly ever eat out because it costs so much.
>
> **D** That's true, but I really ⁶ _____ think we should move. All my friends live round here.
>
> **M** You'll make new friends.
>
> **D** Yes, but it isn't the same ... What about school? Don't you ⁷ _____ that schools in Sydney are better?
>
> **H** I don't think that's true, actually. I ⁸ _____ sure there are good schools outside Sydney, too.
>
> **S** It's OK, as ⁹ _____ as I'm ¹⁰ _____ ... as long as the internet connection is good.

PRONUNCIATION   sentence stress

4a **1.7))** Listen and circle one stressed word per phrase.

1 As far as I'm concerned ...

2 Some people say that ...

3 I really feel that ...

4 If you ask me, ...

5 How do you feel about ...?

6 Don't you think ...?

b **1.8))** Listen to the complete sentences. Pause the listening and repeat after each sentence.

Writing   social media

5a Follow the instructions to make sentences 1–4 into texts suitable for social media.

- Cross out three unnecessary words in each sentence.
- Replace two words with letters or numbers in each sentence.
- Abbreviate one word in each sentence.

1 ~~I will~~ see you at ~~the~~ birthday party.
   c u   *bday*
   c u at bday party

2 Sorry, but I have to be in London on Saturday.

3 I am one hour late for work because of the traffic.

4 I have just realized that some people are so rude and selfish!

b Now write the texts from exercise **5a** next to the appropriate hashtags below.

1 #havingfuntonite _c u at bday party_

2 #crowdedbus _____

3 #angrybossahead _____

4 #cousinswedding _____

I can ...	Very well	Quite well	More practice
use noun suffixes.	○	○	○
ask for and give opinions.	○	○	○

2.1   I'll never forget that day

Vocabulary   describing past experiences

1a   Choose the correct options to complete the questions from interviews with people who have dangerous jobs.

1   Do you think the animals *recognize* / *remind* you?

2   Do you *wonder* / *believe* anybody who likes cleaning could do your job?

3   Have you ever *recognized* / *realized* that you were risking your life because you were too close to the heat?

4   Should you always *expect* / *realize* an animal to attack you, or are they less dangerous than they seem?

5   Do you *wonder* / *remember* the first time you heard the alarm?

6   Do you ever have to *remember* / *remind* the people inside the buildings that you are there?

7   Do you ever *wonder* / *expect* how they feel about all these visitors?

b   Which questions would you hear in an interview with …

a   a safari guide?   _1_ , ___ , ___

b   a firefighter?   ___ , ___

c   a window cleaner?   ___ , ___

2a   Complete the answers with the correct form of the words in the box.

> believe   expect   realize   ~~recognize~~   remember   remind
> wonder

a   Well, usually they're fine; but after some time, you learn to _recognize_ the signs that they're stressed, like the way they walk or the sounds they make.

b   Yes! I usually make a noise or something. I _____ once a couple were having a terrible argument, and when they saw me, they just kept going! It's none of my business, anyway.

c   Of course! It was my first day, and I wasn't _____ it – I didn't even have my uniform on!

d   A lot of times. When I started, my colleagues always _____ me to stay at a safe distance.

e   Sometimes I do. Once a lion got really close to me and looked me in the eye. I _____ he knew exactly who I was.

f   Yes, but I try to make all the tourists _____ that this is the animals' home, not ours!

g   No way! Most people can't even go up a high ladder! But I _____ why people are so afraid of heights. With the right equipment, it's perfectly safe. And the view's fantastic!

b   Match the questions in exercise **1a** to the answers in exercise **2a**.

1   _e_   4   ___   6   ___
2   ___   5   ___   7   ___
3   ___

c   **2.1**))) Listen and check.

Grammar narrative forms

3a Read a newspaper article about a lucky escape. Underline four verbs in the past continuous and circle nine verbs in the past simple.

The best DVD ever

Barry McRoy likes movies, but he never ⟨thought⟩ that a DVD ¹_____ would save his life.

Fire and Rescue Director Barry McRoy was walking out of a restaurant one day when two men ran past him. They were fighting over a gun ²_____. One of them shot it and the bullet hit Barry in the chest. Luckily, he was carrying a DVD in his shirt pocket. ³_____. Amazingly, he only realized ⁴_____ while he was talking to the police, when he noticed a hole in his jacket.

Barry wasn't hurt, but the incident completely destroyed the DVD, which left him feeling a bit disappointed ⁵_____!

b Put sentences and phrases a–e in the correct position in the text in exercise **3a**.

a what had happened _4_
b A friend from work had recorded a TV programme for him the day before ___
c because he hadn't watched it yet ___
d which a colleague had given him ___
e because they'd had an argument ___

c **2.2**)) Listen and check.

4 Choose the best verb tense to complete the text about Steve and Julia's unlucky honeymoon.

Steve and Julia didn't have the honeymoon they ¹*were always dreaming* / ⟨*had always dreamt*⟩ of. When they arrived at the airport, their flight ²*took / had taken* off. They had to catch another flight later on and ³*missed / were missing* most of the first day of their honeymoon.

There was another problem when they arrived at their hotel. While they ⁴*were waiting / waited* for a room, one of their bags ⁵*had disappeared / disappeared*. Fortunately, it was returned soon after – one of the other guests ⁶*was taking / had taken* it by mistake.

They decided to enjoy the rest of the day and visit the city centre. They ⁷*were going / had gone* back to the hotel when it started to rain heavily. The taxi driver said he ⁸*hadn't seen / didn't see* such bad weather in a long time.

It ⁹*rained / had rained* most of the week they were there; but fortunately, they ¹⁰*had already gone / went* back home when a hurricane hit the island. While they ¹¹*were watching / had watched* the news at home, they felt really lucky after all.

PRONUNCIATION *be* and *have*

5a **2.3**)) Listen to six sentences. Underline the weak forms of *be* and *have* and circle the strong ones.

1 When I got home, my wife <u>had</u> cooked my favourite dish.
2 In my childhood, I ⟨had⟩ a dog called Spot.
3 At the end of the day, he was exhausted.
4 Thanks, I was looking all over the place for that!
5 Actually, we have enough time to get there.
6 They were good friends at school.

b Match sentences 1–6 in exercise **5a** to reasons a–c.
a Weak form because it is an auxiliary verb: _1_ and ___
b Strong form because it is the main verb: _2_ and ___
c Weak form even though it is the main verb: ___ and ___

c **2.3**)) Listen again. Pause the listening and repeat after each sentence.

I can …	Very well	Quite well	More practice
talk about past experiences.	○	○	○
structure a narrative.	○	○	○

2.2 Unbelievable?

Grammar sequencing events

1a Put the lines in the correct order to make the story of a famous broadcast.

The War of the Worlds

_____ listening to the radio. The music was interrupted to announce an alien invasion. **During**

__10__ actually believed the news was true.

_____ of the broadcast, but many people were not paying attention. **By the**

_____ the live broadcast, reporters interviewed people who had seen the aliens. **As soon**

__1__ On October 30, 1938, millions of New Yorkers had the shock of their lives **while**

_____ **Meanwhile**, others went to the streets with their guns. What most people didn't find out

_____ **as** the first part ended, thousands of people started calling the radio station and the police.

_____ novel, _The War of the Worlds_. The radio station had actually announced this at the beginning

_____ **time** the programme ended, there was general hysteria. It is estimated that over one million people

_____ **until** much later was that it was a hoax, an adaptation by director Orson Welles of a famous

b **2.4**))) Listen and check.

2 Complete the sentences about Orson Welles with some of the words or phrases in bold from exercise **1a**.

1 He had a lot of difficulties _during_ his childhood: his parents divorced when he was four; his mother died when he was nine; and then his father died when he was thirteen.

2 Although he had directed quite successful films, he didn't become really famous _____ the broadcast of _The War of the Worlds_, in 1938.

3 _____ the broadcast finished, Orson Welles became an international celebrity.

4 In 1943, _____ he was living in Hollywood, he married Rita Hayworth, one of the greatest actresses of her time.

5 In 1947, Welles divorced Rita and moved to Europe for ten years, where he continued working as a director and actor. _____, Rita got married again, to a Pakistani prince.

6 _____ he died, in 1985, he had directed thirteen films, including _Citizen Kane_, considered one of the greatest films in cinema history.

3 Correct the mistakes in the sentences.
1 A seven-year-old boy disappeared ~~meanwhile~~ _while_ he was playing in the garden.
2 His mother called the police as soon she noticed he wasn't there.
3 In the time the police arrived, the neighbours had already started looking for him.
4 Several groups searched the area. In meanwhile, a police officer interviewed the parents to identify possible suspects.
5 Everybody believed he had been kidnapped until that the family dog found him.
6 He had been hiding in a tree in the garden while the whole search. He said it was an April Fools' Day joke!

4 Complete the story about the Roswell UFO (Unidentified Flying Object) incident by adding the word or phrase in brackets at the end of each sentence in the correct position.
1 On 25 June 1947, a pilot saw several objects∧ _while_ he was flying over Washington. (while)
2 A farmer in New Mexico claimed he had found part of a flying disk. (meanwhile)
3 He contacted the sheriff and kept the object the Armed Forces took it away. (until)
4 Journalists from all over America flew to the area a local newspaper printed the story. (as soon as)
5 Stories about aliens had already spread the US Air Force declared that the object wasn't a UFO but a weather balloon. (by the time)
6 More mysterious evidence and reports came up the following years. (during)

Vocabulary communication

5a Choose the correct options to complete sentences 1–5 and a–e about April Fools' Day hoaxes.

April Fools' Day

1 April is a traditional day for playing tricks, and every year reputable companies and organizations join in the fun.

1 In 1957, the BBC *announced* / *told* that Swiss farmers were going to have an excellent spaghetti crop that year. _c_

2 In 1976, BBC Radio 2 *admitted* / *interviewed* an astronomer who said that at 9.47 that morning, due to an astronomical event, gravity on Earth would change. ___

3 In 1998, Burger King *invented* / *claimed* they would launch a hamburger specially designed for left-handed people. ___

4 In 2008, a BBC documentary *reported* / *informed* a revolutionary discovery: a group of penguins that had learnt how to fly. ___

5 In 2000, Google said they had *invented* / *mentioned* a new machine called MentalPlex. ___

a He *told* / *reported* the listeners that if they jumped in the air at that exact time, they would float for a while.

b All the users had to do was *keep* / *admit* quiet while the program read their minds.

c They only *informed* / *admitted* it was a joke after hundreds of people called the radio station asking how to plant the crop.

d The documentary *mentioned* / *told* that the birds flew to South America in the winter.

e The advertisement *informed* / *claimed* customers that the ingredients were rotated 180 degrees.

b Match sentences 1–5 to a–e in exercise **5a**.

6 Complete the sentences with the correct form of the words in brackets.

1 A doctor in Cleveland, USA, _claimed_ that he had developed a vaccine for breast cancer. However, when he was _____ by our local reporter, he _____ that, unfortunately, it wouldn't be ready for another ten years. (admit, claim, interview)

2 Arsenal _____ yesterday that Puma will become the team's official sponsor from July onwards. The 150-million-pound deal is _____ to be the biggest in the team's history. (announce, report)

3 A man was arrested in connection with a bank robbery in Edinburgh last Sunday. A police spokesman _____ our reporter that the suspect _____ during the initial questioning. (keep quiet, tell)

7 Rewrite the sentences using the correct form of the words in brackets.

1 A famous palaeontologist said he had made a revolutionary discovery. (claim)
   A famous palaeontologist claimed he had made
   a revolutionary discovery.

2 Journalists from all over the world wanted to ask him questions. (interview)

3 The National Science Association said he was going to be investigated for fraud. (announce)

4 He didn't say anything during the investigation. (keep quiet)

5 The scientist said he had invented some information to prove his theory. (admit)

6 A national scientific magazine informed readers about the whole story in a special edition. (report)

PRONUNCIATION past simple

8a How are these *-ed* endings pronounced: /t/, /d/ or /ɪd/?

1 admitted _/ɪd/_	4 invented ___	7 informed ___
2 interviewed ___	5 claimed ___	8 reported ___
3 announced ___	6 mentioned ___	

b **2.5**))) Listen, check and repeat.

I can ...	Very well	Quite well	More practice
sequence events.	○	○	○
talk about communication.	○	○	○

2.3 Vocabulary development

Vocabulary comment adverbs

1 Choose the best comment adverb to complete each sentence.

1 In the 1980s, Coca-Cola sales were falling, so not *surprisingly* / *luckily*, company directors decided to do something about it.

2 They asked thousands of people to taste different types of Coke. With this information, they introduced 'New Coke', which was sweeter than the original drink. *Fortunately / Curiously*, the public reacted very negatively.

3 The problem was that they stopped selling the old classic Coke. *Remarkably / Personally*, some customers claimed they felt depressed, while others bought large quantities of classic Coke to keep at home.

4 *Fortunately / Sadly*, the company soon recognized their mistake and after seventy-nine days they brought back the original formula.

5 Trying to save 'New Coke', Coca-Cola renamed it 'Coke II', but sales still didn't increase. *Amazingly / Naturally*, the production of the new drink was interrupted soon after.

6 Coca-Cola lost millions of dollars during this period. However, it is possible that the company benefitted in the end, because *interestingly / unfortunately*, sales increased significantly after the incident.

PRONUNCIATION intonation

2a **2.6**))) Listen and repeat these phrases.

1 Fortunately, it wasn't serious.

2 He said that, personally, he didn't mind.

b Mark the intonation ⤴ ⤵ in the sentences.

1 The accident was serious, but luckily, no one was hurt.

2 Unfortunately, there's nothing I can do about it.

3 I got the recipe wrong, but surprisingly, everybody loved the dish.

4 Amazingly, the magician reappeared at the back of the theatre.

5 They invested a lot in marketing, but interestingly, sales continued falling.

c **2.7**))) Listen and check. Then listen again, pause after each sentence and repeat.

3 Read the advice from experts and complete it using the words in the correct form.

Ask the **expert**	
Having problems with anything, from pets to investments? ¹ *Fortunately* , we can help you. Leave a message with your problem and we'll contact an expert to help you out.	~~FORTUNATE~~
Mark I'm thirty-five and don't do any exercise, because I work long hours. ² _____, I haven't had any major health problems so far, but I'm not getting any younger! What do you suggest?	LUCK
Aisha (personal trainer) Not ³ _____ that's a very common problem nowadays, especially in big cities. I recommend cycling to work, or getting off the bus some stops before and walking.	SURPRISE
Erik How should I choose the best internet browser for me? ⁴ _____, I want a fast one, but what other issues are important?	NATURAL
Li (computer programmer) That depends on lots of things, such as what you need it for and how good you are with technology. ⁵ _____, I prefer browsers with good customization options.	PERSONAL
Carlos Two of my fish got sick. Their eyes got really big, and ⁶ _____, they died soon after. What can I do to save the others?	SAD
Colin (vet) This is called pop-eye disease. I treated a case recently with antibiotics and, ⁷ _____, the problem completely disappeared in three days.	REMARK

Vocabulary review

4 Complete the words in the table with the missing vowels.

Verbs for narrative	Verbs for communication
b_e_l_i_ _e_v_e_	_a_ dm _i_ t
__ x p __ c t	__ n n ____ n c __
r ____ l __ z __	c l ____ m
r __ c __ g n __ z __	__ n f __ r m
r __ m __ m b __ r	__ n t __ r v ____ w
r __ m __ n d	__ n v __ n t
w __ n d __ r	k ____ p q _____ t
	m __ n t ____ n
	t __ l l
	r __ p __ r t

2.4   Speaking and writing

Speaking showing interest

1 **2.8**))) Listen to two stories and choose the best title for each.
   1 Saving a baby – twice! / A baby with a special talent
   2 A strange bookshop / A book very far from home

2a Complete the conversations with words from the box.

> amazing believe ~~heard~~ mean really
> someone that way

Conversation 1

A I ¹ _heard_ this incredible story about a baby who fell from a high window on top of a man who was passing by. They both survived, fortunately.

B ² _____ ?

A Wait, that's not all. You're not going to ³ _____ this, but a year later the very same baby fell from the same window onto the very same man.

B How ⁴ _____ ! I don't know what's more unbelievable: the coincidence or how careless the baby's parents were!

Conversation 2

C ⁵ _____ told me about this incredible coincidence with an American writer. She was in a bookshop when she saw her favourite childhood book. She showed it to her husband, and when he opened it, her name was written inside. It was the exact copy she had as a child!

D ⁶ _____ 's incredible!

C Yes, especially considering she grew up in the USA and the bookshop was in Paris!

D What, you ⁷ _____ the book crossed the ocean and she still found it?

C Yeah, decades later.

D No ⁸ _____ !

b **2.8**))) Listen again and check.

3a **2.9**))) Listen and write (I) if the speakers sound interested, and (N) if they don't.
   1 Really? _N_
   2 How amazing! ___
   3 That's awful! ___
   4 What, you mean …? ___
   5 No way! ___
   6 You're joking! ___

b **2.10**))) Listen to the same speakers sounding interested. Listen again and repeat, copying the intonation.

Writing a narrative

4 Complete the story with words from the box.

> ~~ago~~ end instant just soon straightaway while

A few years ¹ _ago_ , Dorothy Fletcher was flying to Florida for her daughter's wedding. She was enjoying the flight, but after a ² _____ , when they were over the ocean, she started to feel unwell. Soon afterwards, she had a heart attack.

The flight attendant asked ³ _____ on the speaker system if there was a doctor on board, and, in an ⁴ _____ , fifteen doctors got up and went to help her! They were travelling to a medical conference in Orlando.

They started treating her with the medical kit in the plane, and, at one point, one of the doctors said: 'I think we're losing her.' But ⁵ _____ then another doctor found her pulse again.

She was taken straight to hospital as ⁶ _____ as the plane landed. She then spent a few days in hospital, but in the ⁷ _____ , she still managed to go to her daughter's wedding!

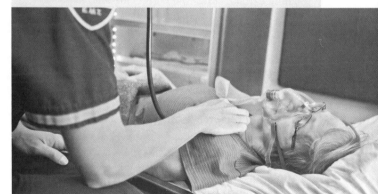

I can …	Very well	Quite well	More practice
use comment adverbs.	○	○	○
engage a listener and show interest.	○	○	○
write a narrative.	○	○	○

2.5 Reading for pleasure

Kidnapped

1 Look at the pictures and the title of the story. Predict the type of story you are going to read. Circle the correct answer.

   1 a romantic love story

   2 a crime story set in modern times

   3 a historical adventure story

   4 a true story about a rebellion

2 Read an extract from *Kidnapped*, a famous novel set in Scotland in the eighteenth century.

3 What do you think happens next to David in the story? How do you know that he didn't die?

Kidnapped

The story so far

After the death of his parents, young David Balfour has gone to live with his uncle at the great House of Shaws in Cramond, near Edinburgh. One day, his uncle takes him to the port at Queensferry. It is there that David makes a surprising discovery – his uncle was younger than his father, so the great House of Shaws should really belong to David.

I had thought that my father was the <u>younger</u> brother, and now I understood why my uncle had lied to me, and wanted to kill me. The house of Shaws had belonged to my father, not my uncle, and now I had inherited it. The poor country boy who had walked from Essendean was the owner of a fine house and farmland! My head was full of the wonderful things that I could do in my life, as I looked, unseeing, at the sea.

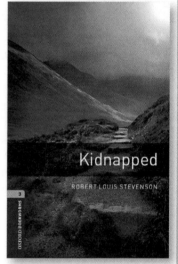

Just then my uncle and the captain came out of the public house. The captain smiled in a friendly way as he spoke to me. 'Sir,' he said, 'Mr Balfour has told me a lot about ye. I'm only sorry I haven't time to get to know ye better. But I'd like ye to come on to my ship for half an hour, before we sail, and have a drink with me.'

Now, more than anything in the world, I wanted to see the inside of a ship, but I remembered that I had to be careful. 'My uncle and I have to see the lawyer, sir,' I replied, 'so I'm afraid we may not have enough time.'

'Aye, aye,' he answered, 'I know, but ye see, the ship's boat can put ye both down near Rankeillor's house, after ye've seen the ship, so ye won't lose any time.' Suddenly he said quietly in my ear, 'Watch out for the old man – he wants to hurt ye. Come and talk about it.' Putting his arm in mine, he said loudly, 'What can I bring ye back from my travels? A friend of Mr Balfour's is a friend of mine!'

By this time we were on the beach, and he was helping my uncle and me into the boat. I thought that I had found a good friend and helper, and I was very excited as we came closer to the great ship, full of busy, noisy sailors. The captain and I were the first to climb up the ship's side, and at the top the captain immediately put his arm through mine and began to talk about the ship.

'But where is my uncle?' I asked suddenly. I pulled myself away from the captain's arm, and ran to the side of the ship. Sure enough, there was the boat returning to Queensferry, with my uncle sitting in it. I screamed, 'Help, help! Murder!' and my uncle slowly turned to look at me.

I did not see any more. Already strong hands were pulling me away. Then something hit my head; I saw a great flash of fire, and fell to the ground.

Old English words
ye = **you**; aye = **yes**

Text extract from *Oxford Bookworms Library Stage 3: Kidnapped*

Review: Units 1 and 2

Grammar

1 Complete the sentences about two internet shopping giants with the correct form of the verbs in brackets.

1 Amazon and eBay, two of the most important online shopping sites, _started_ in the same year: 1995. (start)

2 Since then, both companies _____ enormously. (grow)

3 Pierre Omidyar had the idea for eBay while he _____ dinner with his girlfriend. (have)

4 Jeff Bezos started Amazon in a garage, with money he _____ from his parents. (borrow)

5 All Amazon employees _____ two days every two years working at the customer service desk, even the directors. (spend)

6 eBay _____ new solutions for quicker deliveries. They have recently created eBay Now, with same-day delivery. (constantly/develop)

2 Complete the comments from a magazine column with one word or phrase from each of the boxes below.

| as soon as | by the time |
| during | meanwhile | until |

| agree | hate | own | prefer |
| want |

YOUR SAY:
Web vs High Street

Do you prefer shopping in stores or online? We asked some of our readers, and this is what they said.

✓ I like shops, but I ¹ _prefer_ buying online because I can compare prices. I tried to do that in stores once, but ² _by the time_ I finished, all the shops had closed!

✓ I ³ _____ a food trailer selling burgers and hot dogs, and I work ⁴ _____ very late, so I do my shopping online. The internet never closes!

✓ If I'm buying clothes, I ⁵ _____ to take the item home ⁶ _____ I buy it. I don't want to wait to have it delivered!

✓ I started shopping online ⁷ _____ my pregnancy and never stopped. I ⁸ _____ all the queues in the supermarket, and having to load and unload the car afterwards.

✓ My husband likes shopping in stores, and I ⁹ _____ with him. He takes the kids to the supermarket on Saturday afternoons. ¹⁰ _____, I put my feet up for a couple of hours and relax!

Vocabulary

3 Read this true story about friendship. Complete it by adding one suitable word from the box in each space. There are some words you do not need to use.

| admitted | believes | common | expect | ~~gets~~ | keeps |
| meet | out | realize | reminds | told | touch | up |

A 'chocolate bar' friendship

Seven-year-old Dylan Siegel ¹ _gets_ on really well with his friend Jonah. They have a lot in ² _____, and when they ³ _____ up, they have a great time. Well, most of the time, because Jonah has a serious liver disease which makes his life very difficult.

Jonah's illness is also very rare, and when Dylan found out that researchers needed money to continue studying it, he decided to help them ⁴ _____. He wrote a book called *Chocolate Bar*, which has raised more than $750,000 in just over a year!

Researcher Dr David Weinstein ⁵ _____ that he had initially thought David's desire to help was 'cute', and he didn't ⁶ _____ a big donation from it. How wrong he was. As he says: 'He's raised more money for this disease than all the medical foundations combined. Ever.'

He also ⁷ _____ that, with Dylan's donation and all the media attention the story has received, a cure might be found.

Dylan uses the phrase 'chocolate bar' to describe something 'awesome'. He ⁸ _____ our reporter that helping his friend Jonah was 'the biggest chocolate bar ever'.

Speaking

4 Complete the conversations with one word in each gap.

1 A ¹ _How_ do you feel about social networking?

B A waste of time, if you ² _____ me.

A Really? Don't you ³ _____ it brings people together?

B Definitely not! Just look at the people in this room: everybody's on their mobile phone!

2 A How do you ⁴ _____ about having more special offers next month?

B Well, according ⁵ _____ our research, price isn't the problem, so why make our products cheaper?

3 Life skills

3.1 Challenges

Vocabulary challenges and success

1 Choose the correct option to complete the sentences.

1 Penny was losing, but she didn't give *in / at / on*. She tried really hard and won the match in the end.

2 When he was young, Tom avoided thinking *for / about / to* getting a job. He preferred to have fun!

3 You really should *make / do / go* an effort to meet people and go out more.

4 One way of dealing *over / with / at* problems at school is to discuss your concerns with a teacher.

5 Amy will never get a job if she just waits *for / at / over* somebody to give her one.

6 Listen to the advice of older people. It's the best way of *making / having / doing* the right choices in life.

7 If you can't find the job you want, *show / be / have* patient and wait until the right opportunity comes along.

8 Strong-minded people *lift / prove / rise* to challenges in life.

➔ **STUDY TIP** We use the verb *make* in the expressions *make an effort* and *make the right choice*. What other nouns collocate with the verb *make* to form useful expressions?

2a Complete the famous quotes with one suitable word. The first letter is given.

1 'I can r_resist_ everything except temptation.' ***Oscar Wilde*** *Irish poet and playwright*

2 'Writing is a form of therapy; sometimes I wonder how all those who do not write, compose or paint can m_____ to escape the madness ... (of the) human condition.' *Graham Greene English novelist*

3 'It is no use saying, "We are doing our best". You have got to s_____ in doing what is necessary.' ***Winston Churchill*** *British politician*

4 'The aim of the wise is not to secure pleasure, but to a_____ pain.' ***Aristotle*** *Greek philosopher*

5 'Nothing makes me so happy as to o_____ nature and to paint what I see.' ***Henri Rousseau*** *French painter*

6 'Some are born great, some a_____ greatness, and some have greatness thrust upon them.' ***William Shakespeare*** *English playwright*

b 3.1))) Listen and check.

3 Complete the text using one word from box A in the correct form and one word from box B in each space.

| A | manage succeed think prefer ~~give~~ rise wait |
| B | to (x3) in (x2) about for |

Improving your willpower

In his book, *Willpower: Rediscovering Our Greatest Strength*, co-written with *New York Times* science columnist John Tierney, psychologist Roy Baumeister argues that every time we resist temptation, our willpower gets weaker and weaker until we can't resist any longer and we **1** _give in_ and eat that chocolate, or buy that handbag. So, he asks, how can we **2** _____ the challenge of choosing to eat, buy or do the right thing? In Baumeister's view, the way to improve your willpower is to avoid **3** _____ things you really want to eat or buy. In tests, people **4** _____ stop bad habits when they had other things on their minds. In one test, for example, he told people to sit up straight every time they sat down. Because they had to concentrate on keeping their back straight all the time, the people in the test didn't have time to think about bad habits. By doing tasks like this one, and by **5** _____ doing them well, the people in the tests learnt how to control their bad habits. They learnt to **6** _____ lunch instead of eating between meals, for example. Although most of us **7** _____ eat that chocolate immediately rather than not eat it at all, it is possible to teach ourselves how to resist.

18 | O⊷ Oxford 3000™

Grammar ability

4 Choose the correct options to complete the sentences.

1 I _____ play football well, but I'm not very good at tennis.
   a (can)   b manage   c am able

2 Tom was late because he didn't _____ to catch the bus on time.
   a able   b manage   c can

3 Jerry _____ getting a place on the course.
   a didn't manage to   b couldn't   c didn't succeed in

4 It was difficult, but we _____ open the door and go inside.
   a were able   b could   c managed to

5 I won't _____ to finish my work before the end of the day.
   a able   b succeed   c manage

6 Omar wasn't _____ to leave work early, so he missed the appointment.
   a able   b could   c managing

5 Rewrite the sentences. Use the words in brackets in the correct form.

1 I'm afraid we aren't able to return the documents you sent. (can)
   I'm afraid we can't return the documents you sent.

2 Were they able to find their way back easily? (manage)
   _____

3 Tina couldn't get a holiday job last summer. (able)
   _____

4 Some students managed to pass all the exams. (succeed)
   _____

5 Are you able to lift such heavy bags? (can)
   _____

6 Are you sure that Jack will manage to find the hotel? (able)
   _____

7 Lars didn't succeed in passing his driving test. (manage)
   _____

8 Do you think Anna is able to come on Sunday? (can)
   _____

6 Complete the sentences. Use *can/can't, could/couldn't, be able to, manage to* or *succeed in* and the words in brackets. There is sometimes more than one possible answer.

If at first you don't succeed ...

In the 1920s, a young Japanese engineer applied for a job at Toyota, but he **1** *didn't succeed in getting* (not get) the job, so he decided to start his own business. His name was Soichiro Honda.

When he was young, Ludwig van Beethoven had lots of violin lessons, but he **2** _____ (not play) the instrument very well. He was hopeless at it! So, he decided to become a composer.

In the future, nobody **3** _____ (buy) any of Vincent van Gogh's paintings because they will be so valuable and expensive. In his lifetime, however, van Gogh only **4** _____ (sell) one painting … to a friend.

When Fred Astaire arrived in Hollywood, people said that he had no talent. 'He **5** _____ (not act) and he **6** _____ (not sing)!' said one critic at the time. However, Astaire did have talent. He **7** _____ (dance) really well, and he soon became a star.

Harland David Sanders knew that he **8** _____ (cook) chicken really well. He had a great recipe, but restaurants rejected it 1,009 times before eventually one restaurant decided to use it. He called it Kentucky Fried Chicken (or KFC), and the rest is history.

I can …	Very well	Quite well	More practice
talk about challenges and success.	○	○	○
talk about ability.	○	○	○

3.2 Faking it?

work skills

1 Match verbs 1–6 to words a–f to make transferable skills.

1	work	a	teams
2	make	b	goals
3	manage	c	hard
4	set	d	decisions
5	solve	e	responsibility
6	take	f	problems

2 Complete the text with the phrases in exercise **1** in the correct form.

What makes a **great** football manager?

Managers spend long hours working with their football teams. They have a lot to do, so the ability to **1** _work hard_ is important. Because players and staff need to know exactly what they have to achieve during a football season, managers have to be good at **2** _____ for everybody at the club, including the players and the coach. Managers also need to be very strong people, able to **3** _____ for failure as well as success – if their team loses, they have to talk to journalists and explain what went wrong! Great managers are good at **4** _____ – they can think quickly, and act immediately. For example, they can decide when to change a player or change the formation of the team. They are also good at **5** _____ – and they need to be, because during a football match a lot of things go wrong, and they have to find a solution. It is the ability to change things in positive ways that makes some managers great.

Two great managers are Louis van Gaal, who has **6** _____ all over the world, including Manchester United and the Netherlands national football team, and Pep Guardiola, who has been the boss at Barcelona and Bayern Munich. What makes them so special?

3 Complete the phrases with the verbs in the box.

being (x2)   managing   persuading   tasking   working

1	_managing_	tight schedules
2	_____	well under pressure
3	_____	confident in yourself
4	multi_____	
5	_____	people to do things
6	_____	a good leader

4 Match the phrases in exercise **3** to the descriptions of van Gaal and Guardiola.

Van Gaal or Guardiola
Who is the best football manager?

Louis van Gaal is a strict but emotional manager with three great strengths.

- He is the boss and other people are happy to follow him.   a _6_
- He believes strongly in his own personal abilities.   b ___
- He is good at getting his players to do exactly what he asks them to do.   c ___

Pep Guardiola is a thoughtful and clever manager with many strengths.

- He uses his time well and can prepare teams to play in only a few days.   d ___
- He can do lots of different things at the same time.   e ___
- When journalists and fans criticize him, he never panics. He always does things well.   f ___

Van Gaal and Guardiola are both great managers. Who is the best? You decide.

Grammar obligation, permission and possibility

5 Choose the correct option to complete the text.

The unwritten rules of the workplace

In every workplace, there are official rules that everybody **¹**(*has to*)/ *can* follow, and then there are the *unwritten* rules. The first few weeks in a new job can be demanding because you just don't know what is *really* allowed. In other words, you have no idea what you **²***can / need to* do, and what you **³***can't / don't need to* do.

A friend of mine recently started work in a large design company. The company guidelines were clear:

- You **⁴***can / have to* wear a shirt and tie at all times. Looking smart is obligatory. You **⁵***mustn't / needn't* wear jeans.

- Our company has flexible hours. You **⁶***mustn't / don't have to* start work at nine every day. You **⁷***can / need to* start at any time between eight and ten.

Imagine how my friend felt on his first day when he arrived at nine in his best shirt and tie, only to find that everybody else had arrived at eight, in T-shirt and jeans. The *unwritten* rules said that you **⁸***had to / mustn't* arrive early if you wanted the bosses to think you were an enthusiastic worker, but on Fridays (and my friend's first day was a Friday) you **⁹***didn't have to / couldn't* wear smart clothes. Wearing smart clothes was permitted, but because it was 'dress-down Friday', it wasn't obligatory, and everybody preferred to wear jeans. Employees only **¹⁰***could / had to* dress smartly if they had a meeting with a client.

In a new job, learning the *unwritten* rules can be challenging and embarrassing, but once you've learnt them, you don't forget them.

PRONUNCIATION sentence stress

6a 3.2)) Listen to the unwritten rules and circle the strong stress in each sentence. In which sentences are the modal verbs stressed?

1 You (have) to wear a shirt and tie.

2 You mustn't wear jeans.

3 You needn't start work at nine.

4 You can start at any time.

b 3.2)) Listen again and repeat.

7 Rewrite the workplace rules so they have the same meaning. Use one of the modal verbs in brackets.

1 We're allowed to dress down on Fridays. (can / need to)
   We can dress down on Fridays.

2 It isn't necessary to wear a tie. (mustn't / don't have to)
   You _____

3 A few years ago, employees weren't allowed to check personal emails at work. (couldn't / mustn't)
   A few years ago, employees
   _____

4 You aren't allowed to eat sandwiches at your work station. (couldn't / can't)
   You _____

5 In the past, it was obligatory for employees to sign out every time they left the building. (could / had to)
   In the past, employees
   _____

6 It is necessary to book holidays six months in advance. (can / need to)
   You _____

7 It is obligatory to switch off your mobile phone at work. (could / must)
   You _____

8 From the start of next month, it is permitted to start work between 8 and 10 a.m. (need to / be able to)
   From the start of next month, we
   _____

I can …	Very well	Quite well	More practice
talk about transferable skills.	○	○	○
talk about obligation, permission and possibility.	○	○	○

3.3 Vocabulary development

Vocabulary | compound adjectives

1a Complete the compound adjectives with verbs from the box using *-ing* forms and past participles.

> hand ~~know~~ look make price sleeve
> speak work

1 a well-*known* actor
2 a left-_____ tennis player
3 a short-_____ jacket
4 a good-_____ man
5 an English-_____ tour guide
6 a home-_____ cake

b Match the phrases in exercise **1a** to descriptions a–f.

a She's won a lot of matches because of her unusual style of play. *2*
b It's very fashionable, but her arms get cold when she wears it. ___
c I think he's a male model. ___
d She told us all about the history of the palace, and I understood every word! ___
e He's been in lots of Hollywood films and has won an Oscar. ___
f It's full of fruit and tastes better than anything you can buy in a supermarket. ___

2 Complete the text with compound adjectives formed from the words in the box.

> 500 easy ~~fifty~~ five full going hand hard ~~minute~~
> over page priced second star time working

The first day at work

Congratulations! Having survived that demanding ¹ *fifty-minute* interview, you've finally got the job you always wanted, and it's a ² _____ job, too, so you'll be working nine to five. Tomorrow is your first day. So, how do you make a good impression? It doesn't matter whether you have a job in a ³ _____ shop, selling old clothes and books, or a ⁴ _____ hotel, dealing with very rich guests prepared to pay £10 for an ⁵ _____ coffee in the luxurious bar, because whatever your job, you need to dress

smartly, smile broadly and look confident when you arrive. You want your colleagues to think you are a friendly and ⁶ _____ person, and you want your boss to think you're ⁷ _____, so look busy and keen to do as much as you can. You need to get to know people, remember names, and ask questions, too; and if your new employer has given you a huge ⁸ _____ manual to read, make sure you read it! Remember that your colleagues will be judging you from day one, so make sure they judge you well.

Vocabulary review

3 Match verbs 1–8 to words a–h.

1	make	a	with all the problems
2	make	b	for people to arrive
3	deal	c	the right choices
4	rise	d	to resist temptation
5	think	e	to the challenge
6	succeed	f	an effort to work hard
7	wait	g	in achieving your goal
8	manage	h	about what you want to do

4 Complete the job advertisement with words from the box.

> being making managing setting solving taking
> tasking ~~working~~

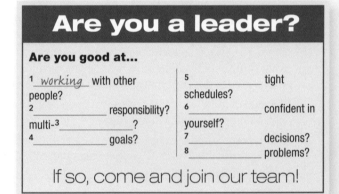

Are you a leader?

Are you good at...

¹ *working* with other people?
² _____ responsibility?
multi-³ _____?
⁴ _____ goals?
⁵ _____ tight schedules?
⁶ _____ confident in yourself?
⁷ _____ decisions?
⁸ _____ problems?

If so, come and join our team!

3.4   Speaking and writing

Speaking   practical instructions

1a   **3.3**))) Listen to an environmental scientist describing how to make a cardboard solar cooker. Tick the materials that are used.

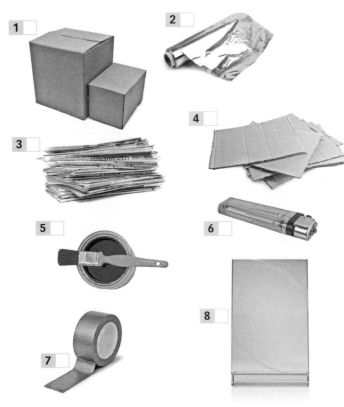

1
2
3
4
5
6
7
8

b   **3.3**))) Complete the questions and instructions with one word in each space. Listen again and check your answers.

1   How do you _make_ the cooker?
2   Let me _____ you.
3   The first _____ you do is place this larger box in front of you ...
4   Can you _____ me?
5   You do it _____ this.
6   When you've _____ this, use the black paint to paint the inside ...
7   After _____ this, cover the sides of the box with the aluminium foil.
8   OK, what _____?

Writing   writing an opinion paragraph

2a   Read the paragraph from an essay and choose the best word to complete the title.

The best way to learn is by _____.
a   reading   b   speaking   c   doing

b   Complete the text with phrases from the box.

also   for example   ~~for instance~~   on top of that
such as   too

DO AND LEARN

Some people argue that we learn most from studying textbooks. However, it seems to me that the most memorable way of learning is by physically taking part in activities. If you want to learn how to play tennis, [1] _for instance_ , reading books about how to serve is a waste of time. You have to get out there on a tennis court and start practising. Learning useful practical skills, [2]_____ taking part in a debate or interviewing people, can only be learnt by actually doing them, [3]_____.
So, what about traditional school subjects like history or geography? Well, I agree that you need books, but I believe they are [4]_____ best learnt in active ways. Students can learn about geography by going on field trips to study rocks or rivers, [5]_____; and they can learn about history by exploring old buildings, going to museums or handling old objects. Learning in this way is natural and instinctive. It is how our ancestors learnt. [6]_____, it is a way of learning that is both fun and memorable. As the old proverb says: 'Tell me and I forget, show me and I remember, involve me and I understand.'

I can ...	Very well	Quite well	More practice
use compound adjectives.	○	○	○
give practical instructions.	○	○	○

4 Space

4.1 Living on water

living on water

1 Choose the correct answer to each question.

1 Which one is usually bigger?
   a the sea   b the ocean

2 Which one is not near the sea?
   a a beach on the coast   b a lake inland

3 Which one is a type of boat?
   a a ferry   b a canal

4 Which phrase means you are travelling across the sea or ocean on a boat?
   a in sea   b at sea

5 Which of these is surrounded by the sea on all sides?
   a an island   b the mainland

6 Which plants grow in water?
   a cacti and pine trees   b reeds and rice

2 Match the headings from an advertising brochure to the correct text.

1 TAKE THE FERRY TO YOUR HOLIDAY DESTINATION

2 GO ON AN EXCITING HOLIDAY ACROSS THE OCEAN

3 HAVE FUN ON A CANAL HOLIDAY

4 ENJOY A SPECIAL BEACH HOLIDAY

5 HEAD INLAND TO VISIT OUR LAKES AND FORESTS

a After twelve days at sea, we reach Bermuda, where there will be time to visit the beautiful island …

b Relax on the beach, swim in the sea and enjoy the bar, the restaurant and volleyball …

c It's the best way to make the short, one-hour crossing from the mainland to the island …

d There's more to Corsica than sand and waves, so rent a car, leave the coast and take a look at its natural beauty …

e Spend a week travelling slowly through England's beautiful countryside on the man-made system of waterways …

3 Complete the article with words from the box.

➡ **STUDY TIP** Make sure you look at the words on both sides of the gaps before deciding which word fits in each gap.

beaches   canals   coast   ~~ferry~~   floats   inland   island
mainland   sea   waves

The world's largest ferry

Every summer, the world's largest car **1** _ferry_ carries holidaymakers and their cars across the **2**_____ from Holyhead to Dublin. The port of Holyhead is on the west **3**_____ of the small **4**_____ of Anglesey, in Wales. Dublin is both a port and the biggest city on the Irish **5**_____ . The ferry's name is the *MS Ulysses*; it is over two hundred metres long and about fifty metres high, and it can carry 2,000 passengers and crew, and approximately 1,500 vehicles. How it **6**_____ on the water with so many cars on board is a miracle of engineering! Once the ferry arrives in Dublin, holidaymakers head for the city, or for the sandy **7**_____ on the coast. The sea off the coast of Ireland is great for surfing, especially in Sligo and Donegal. Surfers love the huge, powerful **8**_____. Other holidaymakers drive **9**_____ towards the hills and villages of central Ireland to enjoy walking or cycling holidays; or they rent a narrow boat to explore the **10**_____, the many waterways that go across the country. Thanks to the world's largest ferry, getting to Ireland is easy, and there is plenty to do once you get there.

Grammar *will/be going to* for predictions and decisions

4 Choose the best future form to complete the sentences.

1 There are no clouds in the sky. It *won't* / *isn't going to* rain today, so let's go to the beach.

2 In the future, ordinary people *won't* / *aren't going to* be able to travel abroad as inexpensively as people do now.

3 The tourist board have plans for the island. They *'ll* / *'re going to* build new hotels there.

4 Your suitcase looks really heavy. I *'ll* / *'m going to* carry it upstairs for you if you like.

5 We've had a look at the brochure and decided on a hotel. We *'ll* / *'re going to* stay on the coast.

5a Read the extract from a radio travel programme. Complete the sentences with *will* or *going to* in the correct affirmative form. Use contractions with pronouns as in the example.

TRAVEL THE WORLD

Next week, on Travel the World, I ¹ *'m going to* visit an unspoilt island in the Pacific where islanders face a difficult choice. A major hotel chain has offered a lot of money to build a luxury hotel, and they ² _____ start construction next year. At least, that's their plan. The islanders have the final say, and they ³ _____ hold a meeting to discuss all the issues. We hope to be there to hear what they think. Currently, nobody knows what they ⁴ _____ decide to do. Many people believe that tourism ⁵ _____ bring unwanted pollution and large, ugly buildings to the island. At the same time, others believe it ⁶ _____ create jobs and introduce shops and services. On other islands nearby, for example, the arrival of tourism has resulted in the destruction of coral reefs and the islanders' traditional way of life; but people are richer and have more opportunities. Clearly, the choice isn't an easy one. I ⁷ _____ see you next week. Goodbye from paradise.

b **4.1**))) Listen to the extract and check.

6 Read the responses of six holidaymakers to the question *What are your holiday plans this year?* Complete the responses with *will* or *going to* and the verbs in brackets.

1 We've just bought a new house, so we can't afford a holiday. We *'re going to stay* (stay) at home!

2 I haven't really thought about it, but I don't think we _____ (go) abroad this summer.

3 We've planned a holiday in Scotland. We _____ (climb) Ben Nevis, the highest mountain in Britain.

4 My boyfriend and I have decided to go to New York in June. We _____ (book) the tickets tomorrow. I can't wait!

5 I never go away on holiday. One day, pollution from carbon fuels _____ (destroy) the ozone layer. That's why I never fly.

6 I haven't thought about it, to be honest. I _____ (tell) you later.

I can ...	Very well	Quite well	More practice
talk about the natural world (water).	○	○	○
talk about plans and predictions.	○	○	○

4.2 Forest bathing

Vocabulary the natural world

1 Match words 1–6 to pictures a–f.

1 rocks   _b_   4 cliffs ___
2 peaks ___   5 soil ___
3 pools ___   6 greenery ___

2 Read the definitions and unscramble the words.

1 something clean and pleasant to breathe in
  fresh air   **shref ria**

2 examples are spring and summer
  _____   **anosse**

3 it's warm and feels good
  _____   **insushen**

4 all you can see when you look across a large area
  _____   **aspdelnac**

5 it can make the sky turn red, pink or orange
  _____   **tunses**

6 the natural beauty that you see around you in the country
  _____   **recysne**

3 Six people are talking about their favourite hills or mountains. Complete what they say with the unscrambled words from exercise 2.

1 I love hiking in the Peak District in England. It's an unspoilt _landscape_ of steep hills and green fields.

2 My favourite _____ in the Pyrenees, on the border between Spain and France, is spring. The snow has gone and the mountains are covered in flowers.

3 Up in the Canadian Rockies, you feel so healthy, breathing in the _____.

4 After a long day skiing in the Alps, I love to sit and watch the _____. The colours can be awesome!

5 I remember climbing above the clouds on Mount Fuji in Japan. We suddenly had warm _____ on our faces, and it was so bright we had to put on sunglasses.

6 We travelled around Iceland last year and were amazed by the extraordinary _____. The landscape seemed to be from another planet.

4 Complete the text with words from the box.

cliffs   landscape   scenery   soil   valleys   waterfalls

Film set landscape

The Zhangjiajie National Forest Park in China is an amazingly beautiful [1] _landscape_ of high mountains and deep [2]_____. Powerful [3]_____ crash down the sides of steep [4]_____ into a huge lake that lies far below. Around the lake, a lot of plants grow in the rich [5]_____, creating a thick forest. In the park, three thousand natural columns of rock stand like magical towers. The [6]_____ is so spectacular and dramatic that the forest appears to be a place on another planet. And, believe it or not, it is! Zhangjiajie National Forest Park is the setting for the Hallelujah Mountains and the forests of Pandora in the popular 2009 film, *Avatar*.

➡ **STUDY TIP** When you add new nouns to your vocabulary notebook, note down whether they are countable (c) or uncountable (u), for example: *cliff* (c), *scenery* (u).

Grammar probability

5 Choose the word or phrase which expresses the meaning in bold.

1 **not probable**
a will definitely   b (is unlikely to)   c may

2 **certain**
a is likely to   b may   c will definitely

3 **probable**
a might   b will   c is likely to

4 **possible**
a will probably   b may   c is unlikely to

5 **impossible**
a might   b definitely won't   c is likely to

6a Complete the second sentences in 1–6 so they have the same meaning, using the words in brackets.

> **National Tree Week is the UK's biggest tree celebration. Every year, in the first week of December, people across the country plant a tree.**
>
> **Here are six reasons for taking part in next December's event.**
>
> **1** Over a quarter of a million people are to join our celebration this year. (definitely)
> Over a quarter of a million people _will definitely join_ our celebration this year.
>
> **2** We will probably plant more trees than ever before. (likely)
> We _____ more trees than ever before.
>
> **3** Our forests won't survive unless we plant more trees. (definitely)
> Our forests _____ unless we plant more trees.
>
> **4** Over two hundred school and community groups might take part in this year's event. (possibly)
> Over two hundred school and community groups _____ in this year's event.
>
> **5** You may not need them, but our team of volunteers are here to help. (not probably)
> You _____ them, but our team of volunteers are here to help.
>
> **6** National Tree Week may not succeed without the help of people like you! (unlikely)
> National Tree Week _____ without the help of people like you!

b **4.2**))) Listen and check your answers.

7 Read the article about the future of the Amazon rainforest and choose the correct options to complete the text.

SAVE THE AMAZON RAINFOREST

The Amazon rainforest is the largest tropical rainforest in the world, covering over five and a half million square kilometres. It's home to 10% of the world's known animals and plants, but if we continue to destroy the forest as we are doing now, we can be sure of one thing: many of these natural wonders ¹*may not /* (*won't*) survive. Jaguars, giant river otters, tapirs and other animals ²*will / might* almost certainly become extinct in the wild.

So, what can be done to save the rainforest? Today, there are many important projects that aim to protect millions of kilometres of unspoiled Amazon rainforest. These actions could result in two exciting possibilities. One is that we ³*definitely will / may* save many species from extinction. The other very small possibility is that we ⁴*are likely to / might* recover some of the land that was once rainforest.

Here, at Rainforest Survival, we aim to support these vital projects, and that's why we're asking for your help. Please send us your donations. If we don't take action now, the rainforest is ⁵*likely / unlikely* to disappear in our lifetimes, and we ⁶*probably won't / will probably* lose a whole world of wonders.

I can ...	Very well	Quite well	More practice
talk about the natural world.	○	○	○
talk about probability.	○	○	○

Vocabulary idiomatic phrases about places

1 Read the comments and circle the correct words to complete the texts and tweets.

> **Post your comments and tell us what's making you happy right now!**
>
> Finally feeling **¹**(at)/ in / on home and enjoying going out with my new friends at university.
> **Marina** Andalucia
>
> Relaxing in my garden on a summer's day, miles from **²**anywhere / everywhere / nowhere, and looking at the beautiful view!
> **Guido** Liguria
>
> Working from home, so I don't have to travel to an office every day, packed in like **³**fish / sardines / tuna on the bus!
> **Barbara** São Paulo
>
> Tidying my room, getting rid **⁴**at / of / with everything I don't need any more, and making room **⁵**for / from / of more!
> **Detelina** Sofia
>
> I live in a beautiful city, which I know like the **⁶**back / fingers / front of my hand, and where I feel I belong.
> **Mauro** Verona
>
> I've finally settled **⁷**down / in / up with my partner. We got married and now I'm expecting a baby.
> **Marisol** Caracas
>
> Thought I'd lost my passport. I looked all **⁸**for / over / up the place and finally found it!
> **Ahmed** Cairo

2 Read the text and complete it with idioms, using the word in brackets.

Micro apartments

The problem with living in a crowded city like New York is that apartments are hard to find and very expensive. That's why so many young city-dwellers these days **¹** _are making themselves at home_ (make/home) in tiny micro apartments. Some are only 100 metres in size! They are often beautifully designed, with space-saving ideas like making the stairs into a set of drawers! Even so, new tenants soon **²**_____ (run/space) for their belongings, and have to **³**_____ (rid) all the extra clothes and stuff they don't need when they move in. They have to be very tidy because they simply can't move when there are clothes and bags and things **⁴**_____ (all/place). However, although it won't suit a couple thinking of **⁵**_____ (settle), it will suit busy young professionals who work hard, go out a lot and **⁶**_____ (feel/home) right in the heart of New York.

Vocabulary review

3 Match the words in the box to the definitions. There are four words you do not need.

canal coast ferry forest island lake ocean ~~peak~~ rock season steep waterfall

1 the top of a mountain   _peak_
2 the place where land meets sea   _____
3 a type of boat   _____
4 water surrounded by land   _____
5 a man-made waterway   _____
6 a place full of trees   _____
7 spring, summer, autumn, winter   _____
8 land surrounded by water   _____

4 Complete the sentences with a, b or c. More than one answer may be possible.

a at sea   b in the mountains   c on the coast

1 You find waterfalls ...   _b, c_   4 You find beaches ...   _____
2 You find waves ...   _____   5 You find pools ...   _____
3 You find cliffs ...   _____   6 You find soil ...   _____

4.4 Speaking and writing

Speaking enquiries

1a **4.3**))) Listen to conversations 1–4 and match them to the situations.

a Telephone banking ___
c In a shoe shop ___1

b At the dentist's ___
d At a bus stop ___

b **4.3**))) Listen again and complete the sentences and questions with one word or number in each space.

Conversation 1

Thanks for your help, I really _____ it. I'm size _____, by the way.

Conversation 2

Could you _____ me when the _____ leaves?

Conversation 3

I _____ if you could help me transfer £_____ to my new account?

Conversation 4

Just one last _____. It cost me £_____ last time. How much do you think it'll cost this time?

2a Complete the conversation between a receptionist (R) and guest (G) by writing two words in each gap.

R How ¹ _can I_ help you?

G I ² _____ you could give me a wake-up call at 7?

R Certainly. Are you ³ _____ breakfast starts at 8 tomorrow because it's Sunday?

G No, thanks for telling me. OK. ⁴ _____ wake me at 7.30, then?

R Certainly. Can I help you ⁵ _____ else?

G Could ⁶ _____ me when the bus goes to the airport?

R Yes, of course. The airport bus leaves at 10 a.m., 12, 2 and 4.

G OK. Thanks for your help – ⁷ _____ it.

b **4.4**))) Listen and check your answers.

Writing avoiding repetition

3a Read the text about a Norwegian town called Mo. How many times does the writer repeat *Mo, town, old* and *good*?

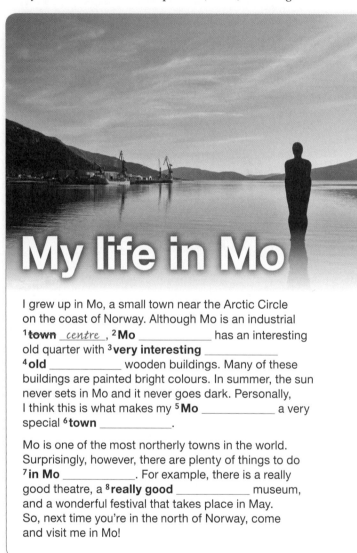

My life in Mo

I grew up in Mo, a small town near the Arctic Circle on the coast of Norway. Although Mo is an industrial ¹**town** _centre_ , ²**Mo** _____ has an interesting old quarter with ³**very interesting** _____ ⁴**old** _____ wooden buildings. Many of these buildings are painted bright colours. In summer, the sun never sets in Mo and it never goes dark. Personally, I think this is what makes my ⁵**Mo** _____ a very special ⁶**town** _____.

Mo is one of the most northerly towns in the world. Surprisingly, however, there are plenty of things to do ⁷**in Mo** _____. For example, there is a really good theatre, a ⁸**really good** _____ museum, and a wonderful festival that takes place in May. So, next time you're in the north of Norway, come and visit me in Mo!

b Make the text about Mo more interesting by crossing out the words in bold and replacing them with words from the box.

~~centre~~ fascinating great hometown it place there traditional

I can ...	Very well	Quite well	More practice
understand idiomatic phrases about places.	○	○	○
make and deal with enquiries.	○	○	○
avoid repetition when writing.	○	○	○

Architect Shigeru Ban

1 Complete the three captions with the words in the box.

architect   architecture   ~~cardboard~~   designs
paper tubing   recycled   refugees   shelters

The ¹ _Cardboard_ Cathedral in New Zealand was designed by Japanese ² _____ Shigeru Ban, who was born in Tokyo in 1957 and studied ³ _____ in Japan and California.

One of Shigeru Ban's most interesting ⁸ _____ is the Centre Pompidou-Metz, a large museum of modern art in eastern France.

2 **4.5** 》 Listen to an interview with an expert talking about Shigeru Ban's career.

3 Choose the correct options to complete the text.

Shigeru Ban has become ¹*known / knowing* as the 'disaster architect', and for good reason. His architecture is perfect in a ²*disaster / disastrous* zone. In fact, his work became famous when he came up with a ³*result / solution* to the desperate need for shelters in ⁴*question / refugee* camps in the early 1990s. Refugees who have lost their ⁵*homes / houses* often don't have enough ⁶*stone / wood* to build shelters. Ban's solution was to make shelters from paper tubing, and it was perfect. The shelters were cheap, strong, ⁷*easy / hard* to build, and they ⁸*saved / spent* lives.

Ban, who uses ⁴ _____ paper as a building material, has also designed emergency ⁵ _____ made from long rolls of ⁶ _____ to provide housing for ⁷ _____ in war zones.

4 What do you think of the materials Shigeru Ban uses? What are the advantages and disadvantages of using paper to construct buildings?

International Books
18 South Frederick
Street
Dublin 2

MID:····98178
TID:····1527
24-10-2022   14:54:01

BATCH:00001451
ICC

AID:A0000000031010
APP LABEL:Visa Debit

VISADEBIT
XXXX XXXX XXXX 5800

SALE   €72.30

TOTAL
            €72.30

PERMISSION TO DEBIT
ACCOUNT

PIN VERIFIED
AUTH CODE:660400

PLEASE KEEP RECEIPT FOR
YOUR OWN RECORDS

CUSTOMER COPY

Your Receipt – Thank You

INTERNATIONAL BOOKS
18 South Frederick Street, Dublin 2.
01-6799375 FAX: 01-6799376

	Euro
ELT	
9901 x 1	44.80
ELT	
9901 x 1	27.50

Total Sale	72.30
Tendered	72.30
Change	0.00

24/10/2022 14:54:32
Total number of items sold =   2
Cashier :   Eric
Paid By :   Access   2

        Sale ID   270265

        WWW.INTERNATIONALBOOKS.IE

Review: Units 3 and 4

Grammar

1 Put the words in order to make sentences.

1 Andy / open / able / front door / to / wasn't / the .
Andy _wasn't able to open the front door._

2 get home / we / before / won't / nine o'clock / definitely .
We _____

3 didn't / I / to / the / manage / exercise / finish .
I _____

4 to / all evening / here / you / have / stay / don't .
You _____

5 unlikely / better / to / get / are / they / much / maths / at .
They _____

6 what / she / pass / to / does / need / do / the exam / to ?
What _____

2 Choose the correct options to complete the sentences.

1 You *can't / don't have to* park on the motorway. It's illegal.

2 I've got the job! I *will / 'm going to* start work on Monday.

3 We *will / might* stop for a picnic if it's sunny.

4 When I was a kid, I *couldn't / didn't manage to* swim.

5 I think that in the next fifty years, over half the world's population *will / is going to* be aged over seventy.

6 You *don't have to / mustn't* buy it. I'll lend you mine.

3 Complete the text with the words in the box.

can   can't   couldn't   may   ~~will~~   will   won't

Life under the waves

'One day, we **1** _will_ definitely live underwater.' That's the confident prediction of marine biologist Ian Lewis. 'The technology is already there,' says Lewis. 'We **2**_____ already construct buildings on the sea floor. In the sea off the coast of Florida, for example, there are research laboratories at a depth of eighteen metres. We **3**_____ build those facilities forty years ago. We didn't have the materials. But now, there is no reason why we **4**_____ construct a whole city underwater. We have the ability. All we need is the desire and the money.'

It is just possible that one company **5**_____ have both the desire and the money to build a large underwater complex. They have plans to build an underwater hotel in the Maldives. It **6**_____ have twenty-two rooms and a bar and restaurant – although, of course, it **7**_____ have a swimming pool! There's no point when you can just put on your diving suit and swim out of the front door!

Vocabulary

4 Match the verbs in box A to the words in box B. Then complete the advertisement with the phrases.

A | deal   rise   succeed   take   ~~working~~

B | in achieving   responsibility   to the challenge   ~~under pressure~~   with problems

AIR DIGITAL

We are seeking experienced sales executives to join our team. Candidates must be good at **1** _working under pressure_ to meet tight deadlines, and be able to **2**_____ of selling in a very competitive market.

NEW WAVE HOTEL GROUP

Ambitious hotel manager sought by exciting new hotel group. In your role, you will be expected to **3**_____ for the day-to-day running of a busy hotel and **4**_____ whenever things go wrong.

SHINE SUMMER CAMPS

We seek young people to work with disadvantaged children at our annual summer camps. Together, we can **5**_____ our goal of improving lives and opportunities.

Speaking

5 Put the sentences in the conversation between Dan (D) and Tracy (T) in order.

D Straight? How do you do that, exactly? Can you show me again? ___

T Well, then you fold over these ends. You do it like this. Make sure they're straight. ___

T It's really easy. Let me show you. ___

D How do you make a really good paper aeroplane? _1_

T Sure. Look. After doing this, you just fold the wings back, and there you are, a perfect aeroplane. ___

T Right, the first thing you do is fold the piece of paper in half. ___

D OK, what next? ___

D Thanks, Tracy. Here, I've got some paper. ___

5.1 Universally popular?

Vocabulary going to the movies

1 Choose the correct words to complete the amazing film facts.

1 Actress Judi Dench was only in a very short eight-minute *scene* / *cast* in the film *Shakespeare in Love* (1998). However, she won an Oscar for her *play* / *performance*.

2 In the film *Kind Hearts and Coronets* (1949), actor Alec Guinness *plays* / *sets* eight different *characters* / *remakes*, including an old soldier, a young photographer, and an old lady.

3 *The Wolf of Wall Street* (2013), which *stars* / *plays* Leonardo DiCaprio and Matthew McConaughey, is *set* / *put* in New York but was actually filmed in Spain.

4 *Memento* (2000) is a film with a very complicated *play* / *plot*. It tells the story backwards from the point of view of a man who can't remember anything. The *cast* / *set* includes Guy Pearce, Joe Pantoliano and Carrie-Anne Moss.

2 Match the two halves of the sentences.

1 Hollywood star Bruce Willis often plays action ___c___
2 *Up* is a wonderful animated ___
3 James Cameron spent over $230 million on the special ___
4 Mike Myers and Jim Carrey are both Hollywood comic ___
5 The film *Ocean's Eleven* is a remake ___
6 The character of Princess Fiona in *Shrek* is voiced ___

a of a film from 1960 which starred Frank Sinatra.
b actors who were born in Canada.
c heroes in films, such as *Die Hard* and *Looper*.
d by Hollywood star Cameron Diaz.
e film, made by Pixar in 2009.
f effects for his sci-fi film, *Avatar* (2009).

➔ **STUDY TIP** Write your own personalized example sentences to help you remember new words. For example, write a sentence about a film with great special effects or a film that is based on a book.

3 Read the interview about the Hollywood film *Captain Phillips*. Complete the questions with words or phrases from exercises **1** and **2**. The first letter is given.

1 So, what is *Captain Phillips* about? What's the p*lot* of the film?

Well, it tells the story of what happens when Somali pirates go on board an American ship. It's a true story, and the idea for the film came from a book written by the real Captain Phillips.

2 And where is the film s_____?

Most of the action takes place in the middle of the Indian Ocean near the coast of Africa.

3 Who s_____ in the film?

Tom Hanks plays the main part.

4 What c_____ does he play?

Tom plays Captain Phillips in the film.

5 Can you describe his p_____?

It's amazing. He's one of Hollywood's best actors, and in this film he's brilliant.

6 Does the film have an interesting c_____? Who else is in it?

Oh, a Somali-American actor called Barkhad Abdi, as well as Catherine Keener, Faysal Ahmed and David Warshofsky.

7 Are there any s_____ e_____ in the film?

Well, yes, there are. For example, the film-makers used CGI (computer-generated imagery) to make you think the ship is out at sea.

Grammar *-ing* form and infinitive with *to*

4 Match the pairs of sentence halves, 1 to 5.

1
1 Do you feel like
2 Would you like
   a to go out this evening?
   b going out later?

2
1 Oscar can't afford
2 Anja can't stand
   a to go to a gym.
   b going to nightclubs.

3
1 On Friday, we recommend
2 On Sunday, we hope
   a to eat out at Luigi's pizzeria.
   b having dinner at Pierre's bistro.

4
1 Sally agreed
2 Luisa thought about
   a to join the science club.
   b joining the army.

5
1 Paul enjoys
2 Yves plans
   a to go to jazz concerts.
   b doing dance classes.

5 Complete the strange but real film titles with the correct form of the verbs in the box.

get   lose   ~~smoke~~   talk   try   worry

1 Thank You for *Smoking*

2 We Need _____ About Kevin

3 How to Succeed in Business without Really _____

4 Stop the World: I Want _____ Off

5 Dr Strangelove, or How I Learned to Stop _____ and Love the Bomb

6 Can't Stand _____ You!

6 Complete the review with the correct form of the verbs in brackets.

If you enjoy **1** *watching* (watch) films from around the world, I suggest **2**_____ (take) a look at this year's list of nominations for best foreign language films at the Oscars. The list aims **3**_____ (promote) world cinema, so, in a way, it is a useful recommendation for films that you really should try **4**_____ (see). You won't fail **5**_____ (find) something worth watching. In 2014, at the 86th Academy Awards ceremony in Los Angeles, the nominations included *The Broken Circle Breakdown*, a Belgian film about **6**_____ (fall) in love and **7**_____ (live) together, and a Danish film called *The Hunt*. In the end, however, the Academy decided **8**_____ (give) the Oscar to *The Great Beauty* (*La Grande Bellezza*), a wonderful Italian film that manages **9**_____ (be) both moving and funny. In the film, we see the lives of rich and important people in Rome through the eyes of a writer who seems **10**_____ (be) bored with the beautiful lives around him.

I can …	Very well	Quite well	More practice
talk about different genres of films.	○	○	○
use the *-ing* form and infinitive with *to*.	○	○	○

5.2 Mosquito smasher!

Vocabulary adjectives to describe a video game

1 Put the words in the box in the correct column.

> amusing disappointing dull enjoyable entertaining intelligent ~~ordinary~~ original predictable silly ~~surprising~~ unexciting violent

Positive	Negative
surprising	ordinary

2 Read the extracts from a review of the graphic novel *Map of Days*. Match the positive adjectives in the box to the phrases with a similar meaning in bold.

> amusing enjoyable ~~entertaining~~ intelligent original surprising

1 *Map of Days* by Robert Hunter is a lovingly made graphic novel that **will give you a lot of fun and pleasure**. _entertaining_

2 The illustrations are not only beautiful but **clever** as well. _____

3 In fact, the artwork is of a quality which the reader **doesn't expect to see**. _____

4 I can't remember reviewing another book with so many **ideas that have never been used before**. _____

5 It is the sort of book that **everybody will like reading**. _____

6 It really **made me laugh at times**. _____

3 Match the negative adjectives in the box to the extracts from reviews of graphic novels.

> disappointing ~~dull~~ ordinary predictable silly violent

1 The pictures in *Day to Night* are boring, grey and uninteresting. _dull_

2 Tim Hope is a great graphic artist, so I was really looking forward to his new book, *The Crown*. Unfortunately, however, it isn't as good as his previous books. _____

3 *The Ancient Planet* is a very average graphic novel, which is neither unusual nor special in any way. _____

4 The problem with *Ghosthunter* is that you know exactly what will happen in the end as soon as you have read the first three or four pages. _____

5 *Fighter* isn't suitable for under-18s because there is so much fighting and killing. _____

6 *Zombie Girls* just isn't serious at all. _____

PRONUNCIATION word stress

4a Match adjectives 1–4 to a–d that have the same number of syllables and the same stress pattern.

1 wonderful   a amusing
2 enjoyable   b violent
3 surprising   c entertaining
4 disappointing   d original

b 5.1))) Listen and check your answers.

c 5.1))) Listen again and repeat the adjectives.

O Oxford 3000™

Grammar present perfect simple and past simple

5 Complete the blog with words from the box. Use each word once only.

ago already ~~ever~~ for just last never since

☒

BLOG

My life as an extra

Have you ¹ _ever_ spent the morning in a restaurant with a Hollywood film star? Well, I have – lots of times! In fact, this morning, I've ² _____ had a cup of coffee with Denzel Washington. He was here only ten minutes ³ _____! And ⁴ _____ Thursday, I sat in a café with Reece Witherspoon. But it's not what you think. I'm not their best friend or anything. I'm a Hollywood extra. Extras, or supporting artists, are the people you see in the background in films. I've worked as an extra ⁵ _____ 2010, and I've ⁶ _____ appeared in over thirty films. I hope to be in a lot more. In all that time, I've ⁷ _____ spoken a single word, or been in a scene ⁸ _____ more than thirty seconds! That's the thing about being an extra. We walk up and down silently, or pretend to read newspapers, or look in shop windows. Oh, and we don't get paid much!

6 Choose the correct tense to complete the extracts from an interview with a film director.

1 So far, I *made* / *'ve made* seven films, and I hope to make many more.

2 We *didn't start* / *haven't started* filming the new movie yet. We plan to start on Monday.

3 In the early 2000s, I *wasn't* / *haven't been* able to get funding for any of my film ideas.

4 Over the last ten years, I *changed* / *'ve changed* the way I make films.

5 I *worked* / *'ve worked* with the same cameraman since 2010.

6 I *watched* / *'ve watched* some of my early films last weekend. They weren't very good.

7 Complete the text about the film industry in Toronto. Use the present perfect or past simple form of the verbs in brackets.

HOLLYWOOD NORTH

American film-makers ¹ _have made_ (make) hundreds of films and TV series in Toronto over the years, and it continues to be a major centre of film production. Since 1957, when a Hollywood TV company ² _____ (film) a TV series there, the Canadian city ³ _____ (be) the set for some of the best-known films in the world, including *Twilight* (2008) and *X-Men* (2000). There are two major reasons why Toronto ⁴ _____ (become) such an important filmmaking centre. The first is that it is cheaper to make films there than it is in major US cities, and the second is that Toronto has similar buildings to New York and Chicago. Over the last fifty years, many directors ⁵ _____ (go) to Toronto to film action scenes when they ⁶ _____ (need) tall skyscrapers in the background. In 2008, for example, Edward Norton ⁷ _____ (star) in *The Incredible Hulk*, performing action scenes on the streets of Toronto but pretending he was in New York.

Toronto is also home to an important film festival. Since it began in 1976, many actors and directors ⁸ _____ (visit) the city to promote their films.

I can …	Very well	Quite well	More practice
describe a video game.	○	○	○
use the present perfect simple and past simple.	○	○	○

5.3 Vocabulary development

Vocabulary extreme adjectives

1a Complete the responses with extreme adjectives from the box.

> astonishing brilliant delicious
> enormous ~~exhausted~~ freezing terrible
> terrifying

1 **A** Were you very tired after the race?
   B Tired? We were absolutely _exhausted_ !

2 **A** Ooh, this tomato sauce is really tasty.
   B It's more than tasty. It's absolutely _____!

3 **A** Brrr! It's a bit too cold for me in here.
   B I know. It's absolutely _____!

4 **A** It's a really big house. It has eighteen bedrooms.
   B It's more than big. It's absolutely _____!

5 **A** The horror film was very scary!
   B Yes! It was absolutely _____!

6 **A** She's really clever and got As in all her exams.
   B I think she's absolutely _____!

7 **A** It's raining again. The weather's been really bad this month.
   B It's rained every day! The weather's been absolutely _____!

8 **A** I didn't expect her to win the contest. The result was very surprising.
   B Surprising?! It was absolutely _____!

b **5.2**))) Listen and check your answers. Notice the stress on *absolutely* and the extreme adjectives.

c **5.3**))) Listen and repeat.

2 Choose the correct adjectives to complete the TV guide.

Vocabulary review

3 Complete the questions about a film with the words in the box.

> based cast characters effects remake
> performance ~~plot~~ scenes set star

A What's the ¹ _plot_ ?
B A family move into a house and strange things happen.
A Where is it ²_____?
B In a house on Long Island, New York.
A Who's the ³_____?
B Canadian actor Ryan Reynolds.
A Is his ⁴_____ good?
B Yes – he's really good in the film.
A Who else is in the ⁵_____?
B Melissa George and Philip Baker Hall.
A What ⁶_____ do they play?
B The wife and a priest.
A Is it a ⁷_____?
B Yes, they made the same film in 1979.
A Are there violent ⁸_____?
B Yes! It's a horror film!
A Are there special ⁹_____?
B Yes! The house falls down!
A Is it *The Amityville Horror*?
B That's right!

4 Circle the word with a similar meaning to the word in capitals.

1 FUNNY   a amusing   b surprising   c predictable
2 DULL   a violent   b unexciting   c silly
3 ENJOYABLE   a original   b ordinary   c entertaining
4 CLEVER   a silly   b intelligent c disappointing

Tonight's TV

	7 p.m.	8 p.m.	9 p.m.	10 p.m.
CHANNEL 1	**THE HEALTH SHOW** Today's show gives advice on how to avoid feeling very ¹*tired* / *exhausted* in the afternoon.	**CROWN STREET** Old friends Mo and Alex find it absolutely ²*difficult* / *impossible* to live together.	**GARDENING TODAY** It's a bit too ³*cold* / *freezing* to plant seeds. Alan Marsh explains why.	**FILM: NIGHTMARE ON ELM STREET** An extremely ⁴*scary* / *terrifying* film. Be warned!
CHANNEL 2	**SPACE** A documentary with absolutely ⁵*surprising* / *astonishing* pictures of Jupiter's moons.	**COOKING TODAY** How to cook very ⁶*tasty* / *delicious* biscuits.	**UNUSUAL LIVES** A look at the life of an extremely ⁷*clever* / *brilliant* boy who is already one of the country's leading mathematicians.	**FILM: THE WOLF OF WALL STREET** An absolutely ⁸*good* / *brilliant* performance by Leonardo DiCaprio.

5.4 Speaking and writing

Speaking comparing and recommending

1a **5.4))** Listen to two friends talking about *Empire* magazine's list of the top five films of all time. In which order does Adam place the films?

The Godfather ___

Raiders of the **Lost Ark** ___

Star Wars ___

The Shawshank Redemption _1_

Jaws ___

b **5.4))** Match the two halves of the sentences in boxes A and B. Then listen to the conversation again and check your answers.

A

1 I expected it to be	a you download it …
2 They're all worth	b very dull.
3 I'd recommend	c less predictable, but it isn't really.
4 It sounds	d seeing.

B

1 It's nothing like as good	a very entertaining.
2 It's really worth	b either of them.
3 That doesn't sound	c as *The Shawshank Redemption*.
4 I wouldn't really recommend	d seeing.

2a Match sentences 1–3 to responses a–c.

1 I think *Batman Returns* is the greatest film of all time. _b_

2 Are you disappointed by this film? ___

3 I haven't seen *City of God* yet. ___

a Really? It's worth seeing, you know.

b Mmm … I'm not at all sure about that.

c Yes, I am. It's nothing like as good as I thought it would be.

b **5.5))** Listen to the conversations and check your answers.

Writing a film review

3 Read the extracts from a film review. In which extract or extracts does the writer mention the following?

1 cast ___   3 setting ___
2 plot ___   4 special effects ___

1 [1]*Although / Despite* being based on a comic strip hero, *The Amazing Spiderman 2* is an exciting film for adults as well as kids. It is set in a computer-generated version of New York, and tells the story of young reporter Peter Parker, who fights crime dressed as Spiderman.

2 The lead actors are brilliant, especially Andrew Garfield, who plays the main character, and, [2]*even though / in spite of* his inexperience as a Hollywood actor, gives his best performance to date. Unfortunately, [3]*despite / however*, the latest instalment of the *Spiderman* saga suffers from a complicated storyline and too many characters. [4]*Although / However* the last half hour of the film is really exciting, the first half of the film has too many different stories going on, which makes it hard to follow.

3 This is a film which will appeal to many young people, and they won't be disappointed if they go and see it. [5]*Although / However*, it must be said that [6]*even though / despite* it has great characters and amazing special effects, it is a bit too long and its plot is unnecessarily complicated.

4 Read the film review extracts again. Choose the correct contrast linkers.

I can …	Very well	Quite well	More practice
use extreme adjectives.	○	○	○
use contrast linkers.	○	○	○
compare and recommend.	○	○	○

6 In control?

6.1 Man and machine

Vocabulary machines

1 Choose the correct word to complete the sentences.

1 On your driving test, you have to *park* / *overtake* / *jam* safely at the side of the road between two other cars.

2 I usually drive in the inside *wheel* / *lane* / *junction* of the motorway because I don't like going fast.

3 There was a terrible *overtake* / *brake* / *accident* on the busy motorway and four people were killed.

4 In Germany, there is no speed *lane* / *limit* / *light* on some motorways. You can go as fast as you like!

5 During your driving test, you must keep both hands on the steering *wheel* / *jam* / *brake* at all times.

6 Seven people were badly *busy* / *injured* / *overtaken* in the car accident.

7 The police stopped her because she was driving *in* / *at* / *over* speed on a country road.

8 The traffic *lights* / *jams* / *brakes* aren't working in the city centre, so the police are directing the cars.

PRONUNCIATION /ə/ sounds

2a **6.1**))) Listen and circle the weak syllable with the /ə/ sound.

1 motorway   4 overtake
2 injured   5 driverless
3 accident

b **6.1**))) Listen again and repeat the words.

3a Read texts A–C and match them to text types 1–3.

1 a sales advertisement   3 a newspaper article
2 a road safety leaflet

A

Yesterday evening, one person died and three people were **1** *injured* in a serious car **2**_____ on Scotland's busiest **3**_____. The police closed the road in order to clear away the badly damaged cars. As a result, there was a very long traffic **4**_____ and it took hours for drivers to get home.

B

To get around in the **5**_____ traffic of today's crowded modern cities, when there are so many cars on the road, you need a Smart car. It's quick, light and fun to drive. When you turn the steering **6**_____, the car responds quickly, which is perfect when you want to get about town, or to get away fast when the traffic **7**_____ turn green. And, because it's only 2.5 metres long and 1.5 metres wide, it's easy to **8**_____ in narrow spaces. The Smart car is the car for you.

C

Coach drivers are advised to drive carefully on busy major roads. They should stay in one **9**_____ and only move out to **10**_____ very slow moving traffic. At a **11**_____, they should always slow down, **12**_____ and stop. They should wait until the road is completely clear before driving on.

b Complete texts A–C with words from the box.

> accident brake busy ~~injured~~ jam junction lane
> lights motorway overtake park wheel

→ **STUDY TIP** Use a learner's dictionary like *Oxford Wordpower Dictionary* to find out more about these words. For example, look up *traffic* and find out what part of speech it is, whether it's countable or uncountable and what it collocates with.

Grammar   defining and non-defining relative clauses

4   Choose the correct relative pronouns. If it is possible to omit the pronoun, choose (–). Sometimes more than one answer is possible.

1   The talk about intelligent machines *that* Jack gave was really interesting.
   a   who   b   (that)   c   (–)

2   I met a woman _____ had taken a driverless car for a test drive.
   a   –   b   who   c   which

3   Robots are machines _____ have a form of artificial intelligence.
   a   that   b   –   c   which

4   I have an artificial hand, _____ I've had since a childhood accident.
   a   –   b   which   c   that

5   The title of the book _____ I'm reading is *I, Robot* by Isaac Asimov.
   a   that   b   –   c   who

6   Jenny is the girl _____ car was in an accident.
   a   whose   b   that   c   who

5   Complete the sentences in the fact file about robots with *who, which* or *that*. Add (–) to show that the relative pronoun can be omitted.

Robots – the essential facts!

1   The word *robot* was first used in 1920 in a play by the Czech writer Karel Čapek, **a** *who* wrote science fiction. It comes from *robota*, a Czech word **b** _____ means 'hard work'.

2   The first robot **a** _____ you could programme to perform useful tasks was *Unimate*, **b** _____ was invented by George Devol in 1954. He sold it to General Motors, an American car company **c** _____ used the robot to lift hot pieces of metal.

3   In the 1990s, robots started exploring dangerous places. A robot called *Dante*, **a** _____ was controlled by experts in the United States, went inside the Erebus volcano in Antarctica; and the Sojourner rover, **b** _____ was designed by the National Aeronautics and Space Administration (NASA), went to Mars.

4   The *Roomba* is the first really successful robotic vacuum cleaner. Its makers have sold over eight million of them. People **a** _____ I know **b** _____ hate doing housework just love this machine.

5   In 2012, a robot **a** _____ was able to move its arms, hands and fingers in exactly the same way as a human became the first robot in space. The 'robonaut', **b** _____ was developed by NASA, can perform dangerous tasks **c** _____ people can't do.

6   Join the sentences about an Icelandic company called Össur. Use the relative pronouns in brackets. Use non-defining relative clauses if necessary.

PROSTHETIC LIMBS
THE POWER KNEE IN ACTION

1   Össur is a global company. It manufactures prosthetic limbs. (that)
   Össur is a global company that manufactures prosthetic limbs.

2   The company's engineers have developed many artificial knees. Their designs have won awards. (whose)
   _____

3   American medical engineer Van Phillips sold his famous product to Össur. He designed a carbon fibre prosthetic foot. (who)
   _____

4   Össur sponsors Paralympian athletes. It is something they are proud of. (which)
   _____

5   The Power Knee is just one product. They manufacture it. (–)
   _____

6   During the presentation, we heard about the latest developments in prosthetics. It was held at Össur's headquarters. (which)
   _____

I can …	Very well	Quite well	More practice
talk about machines in our lives.	○	○	○
use defining and non-defining relative clauses.	○	○	○

6.2　Controlling the weather?

Vocabulary　climate and extreme weather

1 Match words 1–6 to words a–f. Which three collocations describe the effects of extreme weather events?

1 crop
2 climate
3 global
4 destroyed
5 high
6 water

a temperatures
b change
c damage
d warming
e shortages
f housing

2 Write the compound nouns in exercise **1** next to the newspaper headlines.

1

> ## FARMERS REPORT POOR QUALITY OF POTATOES IN FIELDS

crop damage

2

> ## EXPERTS SAY WORLD WILL GET ONE DEGREE HOTTER EVERY TWENTY YEARS

3

> ## MORE RAIN IN DESERTS, LESS RAIN IN TROPICS, SAY EXPERTS

4

> ## NOTHING TO DRINK OR WASH WITH IN SOME AREAS

5

> ## FORTY DEGREES ON THE COAST IN HOT SUMMER

6

> ## THOUSANDS LOSE HOMES AFTER DISASTER

3 Complete the text with words from the box. Use plural forms if necessary.

> drought　fire　flood　~~heatwave~~　landslide　storm
> rainfall　wind

In the past, nobody paid any attention if we had high temperatures in April. We just enjoyed the unexpected [1] *heatwave* and went to the beach. Nowadays, however, we worry that it is a sign of climate change. The question, of course, is whether we should be worried. Extreme weather in 2013 and 2014 suggests we really should.

In late 2013 and early 2014, California experienced so little rain and was so dry that it had its worst [2] _____ ever. In the same period, the UK had its wettest period in recent history. Heavy and continuous [3] _____ resulted in terrible [4] _____ because rivers were so high that the water came into towns. Strong [5] _____ came in from the Atlantic Ocean and destroyed buildings.

The fourth worst tropical [6] _____ in history destroyed villages and towns in the Philippines in November 2013. The powerful winds and heavy rain killed hundreds. In Australia, it was so hot and dry that [7] _____ started in the forests and were out of control for days. And in Washington state in the US, many died when, after weeks of heavy rain, a [8] _____ came down a mountain, carrying rocks and soil and destroying all the buildings in its path. It really does seem that the world's weather is changing.

Grammar　present perfect simple and continuous

4　Put the words in order to make statements and questions.

1　for / been / ages / waiting / I've / here .
　　I've been waiting here for ages.

2　film / have / yet / you / the / seen ?
　　_____

3　hasn't / Sally / been / long / there / living .
　　_____

4　they / lunch / had / 've / already .
　　_____

5　stopped / has / yet / it / raining ?
　　_____

6　long / been / how / there / have / sitting / you ?
　　_____

➡ **STUDY TIP** Remember that in English, to make a question the auxiliary verb changes place with the subject, so *I've broken* becomes *Have you broken …?* and *She's been eating* becomes *Has she been eating …?*

5a　Choose the best reply to each question.

1　Why don't you wear that green necklace any more?
　　a （Unfortunately, I've lost it）
　　b　Unfortunately, I've been losing it.

2　Where's Jo?
　　a　Outside. She's worked in the garden all day. And she's still out there now.
　　b　Outside. She's been working in the garden all day. And she's still out there now.

3　Are you and Louise friends?
　　a　Yes. We've known each other for ages.
　　b　Yes. We've been knowing each other for ages.

4　Sarah seems happier these days. Why's that?
　　a　Well, she's done better at school recently. I hope it continues.
　　b　Well, she's been doing better at school recently. I hope it continues.

5　Do you know Carl well?
　　a　Not really. I've only met him twice.
　　b　Not really. I've only been meeting him twice.

6　I haven't seen Ana at the sports centre for ages. What has she been doing?
　　a　Actually, she's broken her arm.
　　b　Actually, she's been breaking her arm.

b　**6.2** 》 Listen and check.

6　Complete the interview with an American hurricane expert with the present perfect simple or continuous form of the verbs in brackets. Use the present perfect continuous whenever possible.

How do you track or follow a hurricane?

Well, we ¹ *have been using* (use) satellites to track hurricanes for many years now. In the last year, weather satellites ² _____ (help) us to find and follow the progress of a number of hurricanes. Fortunately, all of these hurricanes ³ _____ (leave) our region and are no longer dangerous.

Do you only use satellites?

Well, no. Since 1965, the US Air Force ⁴ _____ (use) special planes called 'hurricane hunters' to monitor hurricanes. The hurricane hunters ⁵ _____ (become) very good at collecting information about extreme weather conditions.

What do experts do with the information?

Well, over the past few years, we ⁶ _____ (develop) better ways of using the information from planes and satellites. In the last year, we ⁷ _____ (be) able to use very complicated computer models to show possible hurricane movements. In my opinion, our work ⁸ _____ (save) the lives of between fifty and a hundred people in the last six months.

I can …	Very well	Quite well	More practice
talk about the climate and extreme weather.	○	○	○
use the present perfect simple and continuous to talk about recent events and changes.	○	○	○

6.3 Vocabulary development

Vocabulary — adjective suffixes

1 Circle the noun or verb in each list that goes with the adjective suffix given.

1	-ous	a (nerve)	b type	c stress
2	-y	a success	b health	c accept
3	-able	a cheer	b stress	c rely
4	-less	a give	b care	c ease
5	-al	a stress	b comfort	c person
6	-ful	a colour	b rely	c tradition

2 Complete the sentences with the adjectives you formed in exercise **1**.

1 Jack has an important exam tomorrow. He's feeling _nervous_.
2 Amy never has problems with her computer. It's very _____.
3 We painted the kitchen yellow and orange. It's really _____ now.
4 Ian eats a balanced diet with lots of fruit and vegetables. He's very _____.
5 I wish you wouldn't be so _____ with my things. You lost my keys and now you've broken my mug.
6 You shouldn't ask her such _____ questions. You've only just met!

3 Complete the blog entry by adding the correct suffix to the nouns and verbs in brackets to form adjectives.

Wedding Day Photos

Last September, my wife and I got married. We were both incredibly **1** _nervous_ (nerve) about the day, of course; but in the end, it wasn't **2**_____ (stress) at all. In fact, it was a really exciting day, and one that we will remember forever. The problem is that although our friends took hundreds of **3**_____ (type) wedding photos of proud parents, **4**_____ (cheer) cousins and crazy aunts and uncles doing **5**_____ (fun) things, we don't know what to do with them. They're all on our computer, you see. But is it **6**_____ (accept) to put our photos on a **7**_____ (person) blog or on a **8**_____ (society) networking site? Or should we print the photos and put them in a **9**_____ (tradition) family album? Personally, I think that sometimes the old ways are best. Wedding photos should be in a wedding album that you can put on a shelf and leave to get old and **10**_____ (dust)! What do you think?

PRONUNCIATION — word stress

4a Add the words in the box to the correct list according to the stress.

acceptable careless enjoyable lucky practical sociable ~~social~~ typical

1 ●● stressful, cheerful, _social_, _____, _____

2 ●●●● reliable, traditional, _____, _____

3 ●●● personal, comfortable, _____, _____, _____

b **6.3**))) Listen and check your answers.

5 **6.4**))) Listen and repeat the sentences. Pay attention to the stress in the adjectives.

1 I prefer furniture that is traditional and comfortable.
2 I feel nervous in stressful situations.
3 It was a reliable and successful company.
4 Don't ask personal questions in social situations.

Vocabulary review

6 Complete the phrases with words from the box.

accident ~~at~~ driverless injured jam junction lane lights limit wheel

1 drive _at_ speed
2 on the inside _____ of the motorway
3 stop at a busy road _____
4 stuck in a traffic _____
5 get in a _____ car
6 behind the steering _____
7 the national speed _____
8 the traffic _____ are on red
9 a serious car _____
10 two people were _____

7 Choose the correct word to make compound nouns.

1	climate	a change	b shortage
2	crop	a damage	b storms
3	rain	a rise	b fall
4	heat	a fall	b wave
5	tropical	a storm	b shortage
6	global	a warming	b heating

6.4 Speaking and writing

Speaking changing arrangements

1a **6.5 》》** Listen to two friends changing an arrangement on the phone. Circle the correct answers.

1 Tom and Kerry arranged to …
  a have dinner at Kerry's house.
  b go to a restaurant together.
  c see a film at the cinema.
2 Tom feels … when Kerry changes the arrangement.
  a angry   b disappointed   c ashamed
3 Tom and Kerry agree to change the arrangement to …
  a next Friday.   b Sunday morning.
  c a different Saturday.

b **6.5 》》** Match phrases 1–7 to phrases a–g with a similar meaning. Then listen to the conversation again and tick the phrases that you hear.

1 I can't make it then. _e_
2 How about going another night? ___
3 That's fine with me. ___
4 I'll confirm it with you. ___
5 I'm meant to cook, but … ___
6 I've got something else on. ___
7 Our arrangements have changed, I'm afraid. ___

a I'm supposed to cook, but …
b I'm available then.
c I'll get back to you later in the week.
d Let's go another night.
e I'm not available then.
f There's been a change of plan.
g I'm busy that day.

c Four of these phrases are usually used in formal situations. Underline them.

Writing a professional email

2a Read the emails. Which email is …
  • from a student?   _____
  • from a member of staff? _____

b Complete the emails with words from the box.

apologize help like Many Unfortunately wasn't able wishes wonder

1

To: Hannah Duggan
From: Peter Brown
Subject: RE Sales Report

Dear Ms Duggan,

I wonder if you could ¹_____ me? Unfortunately, I ²_____ to finish the 2015 Sales Report because I was unwell on Thursday and am still not well enough to come in today. I would ³_____ to work on it over the weekend, but I haven't got the sales figures for 2014. Could you please send them to me?

⁴_____ thanks,

Peter Brown
Assistant sales director

2

To: Dr Paul Davison
From: Ashmita Mehta
Subject: RE This morning's lecture

Dear Dr Davison,

I would like to ⁵_____ for arriving late to the lecture this morning. ⁶_____, my train was cancelled and I had to take the bus. As a result, I wasn't there when you handed out the list of sources for next week's essay. I ⁷_____ if I could come and collect it later today or tomorrow?

Best ⁸_____,

Ashmita Mehta
Engineering 2

I can …	Very well	Quite well	More practice
use adjective suffixes.	○	○	○
make and change arrangements.	○	○	○

6.5 Reading for pleasure

The Everest Story

1   Look at the photos of two climbers, George Mallory and Edward Norton, on Mount Everest in the 1920s. What equipment can you see in the photos?

2   Read the extract from *The Everest Story*.

3   Do you know what happens next? Would you like to climb a mountain like Everest?

The story so far

It is 1924. Three experienced climbers, George Mallory, Edward Norton and Howard Somervell, are on Mount Everest, the world's highest mountain, but four of their porters (the Tibetan men who are carrying their equipment) are higher up the mountain, cold, alone and afraid. In this extract from the Everest story, the climbers must rescue the porters before they die of cold …

Saving the porters

'Are you alive?' the climbers asked. 'Can you walk?'

'Yes sir,' a porter answered. 'But we're afraid. It's too dangerous. If we slip, we'll fall and die!'

'If you stay there, you'll die of cold,' Norton said. 'Wait there – we're coming to get you.'

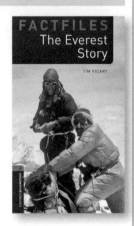

Very carefully, Somervell climbed across the steep slope, towards the four porters. He had a rope round his waist. Mallory and Norton held the rope from below, to keep Somervell safe. But when he was five metres away from the porters, Somervell reached the end of the rope.

'What do I do now?' he thought. 'We have no more rope, and it will soon be dark.'

'Come across!' he called out to the porters. 'It's not far. Carefully, one at a time.'

The first two porters reached Somervell safely. Then they climbed past him, holding the rope, towards Norton and Mallory. Somervell looked at the last two porters.

'Come on,' he said. 'It's not difficult. One at a time.'

But the porters were afraid, and both started together. A second later they slipped and fell. They slid past Somervell down the slope, towards the valley thousands of metres below. But then, a few metres from the edge of the slope, they stopped.

'Don't move,' Somervell said. 'Just wait for me.'

He drove his ice axe deep into the snow. He untied the rope from his waist, and passed it round the head of the ice axe. Then, holding his end of the rope with one hand, Somervell climbed down until he could just reach the men with his other hand. He pulled up the first man, then the second. They climbed along the rope to Mallory and Norton. Somervell tied the rope round his waist again, and climbed back after them.

Even now they were not safe. It was nearly dark, and a long way above Camp 3. One of the porters, Namgya, could not use his hands, because he had bad frostbite. But at last they reached Camp 3, where two more climbers, Noel and Odell, were waiting with warm food.

All the climbers were exhausted. Mallory and Somervell could not stop coughing, and Norton's feet hurt badly. Helping the four porters had made them very, very tired. And they were nowhere near the summit of Everest.

Text extract from *Oxford Bookworms Library: The Everest Story*

Review: Units 5 and 6

Grammar

1 Choose the correct options to complete the sentences.

1 I don't like *drive / driving* really fast.

2 Have you ever thought about *take / taking* your driving test?

3 My van, *who / which* I only bought last month, has broken down.

4 I don't remember the name of the man *who / whose* car I crashed into.

5 We can't afford *to buy / buying* a new car at the moment.

6 I recommend *to take / taking* that car for a test drive.

7 The crash, *that / which* took place early this morning, was reported on the national news.

8 There are a number of drivers – */ that* really worry me on the roads today.

2 Complete the text with the past simple, present perfect simple or present perfect continuous form of the verbs in brackets.

Since it ¹ *began* (begin) in 1978, the *Sundance Film Festival* in Utah ² _____ (be) a showcase for new films from independent filmmakers. At first, the festival ³ _____ (only/show) American films, but since the 1980s, it ⁴ _____ (also/show) feature films and documentaries from all over the world. Over the years, a number of important directors ⁵ _____ (become) famous as a direct result of taking part in the festival. Quentin Tarantino is just one example. When audiences ⁶ _____ (see) his first movie *Reservoir Dogs* at the festival, they ⁷ _____ (love) it. He ⁸ _____ (make) successful movies ever since.

Vocabulary

3 Circle the correct word to make compound nouns.

		a		b		c	
1	rain	a	fall	b	warming	c	slides
2	steering	a	light	b	wheel	c	limit
3	climate	a	warming	b	damage	c	change
4	traffic	a	jam	b	crash	c	brake
5	heat	a	shortages	b	warming	c	wave
6	special	a	effects	b	actors	c	plots
7	action	a	cast	b	plot	c	hero
8	speed	a	road	b	limit	c	wheel

4 Complete the news stories with the words in the box.

~~accident~~ damage injured junction shortages temperatures

There was a serious car ¹ *accident* at the ² _____ between Howard Street and Spencer Road this morning. Two people were ³ _____ and taken to hospital.

As a result of the hot weather, farmers are worried about water ⁴ _____ and crop ⁵ _____ in the region. High ⁶ _____ will continue throughout the week and there is no sign of rain.

5 Complete the sentences with the correct form of the words in brackets. Then choose the correct intensifying adverb.

1 I know exactly what will happen at the end of this play. It's *very / absolutely* _____ (predict).

2 The horror film was *very / absolutely* _____ (terrify)! I screamed!

3 It's *very / absolutely* _____ (freeze) in here. Can we put the heater on?

4 Making a film is a *very / absolutely* _____ (stress) thing to do.

5 Actors often feel *very / absolutely* _____ (nerve) on their first day on the set of a new film.

6 Her performance was *really / absolutely* _____ (surprise). I didn't think she could be so good.

Speaking

6 Order the words to make sentences.

1 I / see / recommend / going / wouldn't / to / it .
   I wouldn't recommend going to see it.

2 be / I thought / than / it's / it would / much funnier .
   _____

3 his / as good / it's / first film / like / as / nothing .
   _____

4 on Saturday / I / the / party / can't make .
   _____

5 I'm / be / to / babysitting / meant / then .
   _____

6 got / afraid / I'm / on / else / I've / something .
   _____

7 I'll / you / confirm / with / later / it .
   _____

7.1 Good prospects

Vocabulary working conditions

1 Match words 1–6 to words a–f.

1	career	a	satisfaction
2	working	b	accommodation
3	be made	c	prospects
4	job	d	redundant
5	rent-free	e	pay
6	holiday	f	hours

→ **STUDY TIP** Word combinations like these are called collocations, which should be learnt as one chunk of language.

2 Read the text and substitute the parts in italics with the collocations from exercise **1**.

Best place in the world to work? Google it!

career prospects

What makes a good job? Salary? **¹**Chances of getting a better job in the future? Job stability (how likely it is to **²**lose your job)? Benefits such as **³**free housing?

Every year, *Fortune* magazine makes a list of the 100 best companies to work for. In 2014, for the third year in a row, Google was at the top of the list. Why? Well, apart from all the benefits you would expect from a big company, such as up to twenty-five days **⁴**of vacation earning full salary, Google offers some other unique advantages:

- Employees can spend up to 20% of their **⁵**time at work on a project of their choice.
- They get free food, gym membership, carwashes and even haircuts!
- They can take their children and even their pets to work.

All this guarantees a high level of **⁶**happiness at work, which makes the internet giant a dream company to work for.

3 Complete the interviewer's (I) questions and candidate's (C) answers from a job interview. The first letter is given.

I Why were you **¹**u_nemployed_ from January to August last year?

C After I was made **²**r_____, I decided to take a management course.

I Are you flexible about **³**w_____ hours and travelling?

C I understand that flexibility is an important part of this **⁴**o_____.

I What type of **⁵**w_____ c_____ would make a difference to you?

C Well, the **⁶**s_____ is very attractive, but health insurance would be a real plus.

4 Complete the answers with words from the box. Which three answers won't help you get the job?

career prospects   job satisfaction   promotion
~~qualifications~~   rent-free accommodation   sick pay

1 I believe my _qualifications_ will be useful to the company.

2 I really want to move out of my mother's house, so I need a job that offers _____.

3 This job is OK, but I'd like to get a _____ soon because I want to earn more money.

4 I'm looking for a job with good _____, and I'm prepared to work hard to achieve my professional goals.

5 The salary's important, but _____ comes first for me. I want to be challenged, work in a lively atmosphere and enjoy my job.

6 I left my last job because I didn't get any _____ when I was ill. It wasn't fair.

Grammar *used to* and *would*

5 Read the text and correct five mistakes. Two examples are correct.

> **There are many websites dedicated to people who have changed careers. Here are some amazing stories from some of them:**
>
> - *From Banking to Fitness* Marie Gregor **¹** *used to* ~~feeling~~ *feel* frustrated as a bank manager, but now she runs a successful fitness business.
> - *From Marketing to Chef* Simon Hunt **²** *didn't used to like* all the marketing courses he had to take, so he decided to retrain as a chef.
> - *From Teaching to Gardening* Gianluca Biaggio owns a gardening business. The only thing he misses from his old job in a school is his friends, who he **³** *would talk* to every day.
> - *From Telesales to Watersports* After Martin Holmes **⁴** *used to go* on a year-long holiday, he knew he couldn't go back to the life he **⁵** *used to have*, so he decided to qualify as a watersports instructor.
> - *From Nurse to Actor* Ben Atkinson's talents were being wasted in the hospital where he **⁶** *is used to work*. Now he works in the theatre, which is his real passion.
> - *From IT to Photography* Susan Wainwright **⁷** *would be responsible* for training people in IT, and now travels the world taking photos.

6a Read some answers to the question: '*Why did you decide to work from home?*' Rewrite five of the sentences using *used to*. Put a cross next to the sentence you cannot rewrite.

1 I spent more than two hours on the bus every day.
   <u>I used to spend more than two hours on the bus</u>
   <u>every day.</u>

2 I didn't see much of my children during the week.
   _____
   _____

3 People interrupted me all the time.
   _____
   _____

4 I was fired and became freelance.
   _____
   _____

5 I hated wearing a tie every day.
   _____
   _____

6 I felt depressed on Sundays, thinking about going to the office the next day.
   _____
   _____

b In which four sentences can you use *would* instead of *used to*?

PRONUNCIATION similar sounds

7a **7.1**))) Listen and repeat.

| used to | I used to go to work by bus |
| they'd | they'd go to work by bus |

b **7.2**))) Listen and tick the sentences you hear.

1 ✓ I used to work at home.
   ___ I use it to work at home.
2 ___ I'd go by car every day. I never walked.
   ___ I go by car every day. I never walk.
3 ___ I used a copy from the Web.
   ___ I used to copy from the Web.
4 ___ I'll travel abroad a lot.
   ___ I'd travel abroad a lot.

c **7.3**))) Listen and repeat the sentences.

I can ...	Very well	Quite well	More practice
talk about working conditions.	○	○	○
talk about finished habits and situations.	○	○	○

7.2 Ask an expert

Vocabulary **high achievers**

1 Choose the best words to complete the quotes about fame and success.

1 'Some succeed because they are destined to. Most succeed because they are *ambitious* / *determined to*.'
Henry van Dyke

2 'It is not enough to be *a hard-working* / *an ambitious* person. Think: what do you work at?'
Leo Tolstoy

3 'Always aim for *achievement* / *awards*, and forget about success.'
Helen Hayes

4 '*An expert* / *A champion* is a person who has made all the mistakes that can be made in a very narrow field.'
Niels Bohr

5 '*An expert* / *A champion* is afraid of losing. Everyone else is afraid of winning.'
Billie Jean King

6 'The desire to reach for the stars is *hard-working* / *ambitious*. The desire to reach hearts is wise.'
Maya Angelou

2 Complete the descriptions of the people in exercise **1** with one word in each group. The first letter is given.

1 Henry van Dyke graduated from Princeton University and a*chieved* success with poems such as *Time is*, which is on the memorial stone in London for the 9/11 victims.

2 Leo Tolstoy was a f_____ Russian writer and philosopher. He wrote *War and Peace*, *Anna Karenina* and other novels.

3 Helen Hayes was an American actress who, in a career nearly eighty years long, won a large number of a_____, including an Oscar, a Grammy, a Tony and an Emmy.

4 Niels Bohr was a Danish physicist whose model of atomic structure brought him f_____ and a Nobel Prize.

5 Billie Jean King was a very t_____ tennis player who was number one in the world and won thirty-nine Grand Slam titles.

6 Maya Angelou was a w_____-k_____ writer and human rights activist who received over eighty honorary doctoral degrees.

3 Complete the text about superachievers with words from the box.

> achieved   achievement   champions   determined
> experts   hard-working   talented   well known

The **Art** of **Doing**

In their book *The Art of Doing*, Camille Sweeney and Josh Gosfield interviewed thirty-six **1** _experts_ to find out how they have **2**_____ so much in life. If you are also **3**_____ to be very successful, here are some things you can learn from these superachievers:

• Working long hours helps, but apart from being **4**_____, you also need to be smart. Superachievers know when they have to adapt to new circumstances.

• Superachievers are **5**_____ for being good listeners. This helps them learn what they need to know about the world around them.

• They tend to be **6**_____ storytellers and good at persuading others. To turn a good idea into a concrete **7**_____, you need to be able to sell the idea to other people.

• Success brings happiness, but happiness also brings success. Most sports **8**_____, for example, really love what they do.

Grammar question forms

4a Complete each question from a radio interview about *The Art of Doing* by adding the word in brackets in the correct position.

1   How many self-help books ⟨*have*⟩ you read? (have)
2   Who you about *The Art of Doing*? (told)
3   You remember where you bought it? (do)
4   Can I ask which your favourite chapter? (was)
5   What in your life after reading this book? (changed)
6   Who you recommend this book to? (would)

b Which of the questions are …

- object questions? _1_ and ___
- subject questions? ___ and ___
- indirect questions? ___ and ___

5a Match questions 1–6 in exercise **4a** to answers a–f.

a   Well, not much so far, but I definitely feel more determined.   _5_
b   Yes, I usually buy books at a store in the city centre, but I got this one online.   ___
c   My mother's Brazilian, so it was the chapter on how Hélio Castroneves became a racing champion.   ___
d   My boss mentioned it in a training session on career achievements.   ___
e   To anybody who wants to achieve more in life, I guess.   ___
f   Not many, but I've read a lot of biographies of well-known politicians.   ___

b **7.4** ⟩⟩ Listen and check.

6 Complete the indirect questions.

1   What's your name?
    Can I ask you what your name is?
2   Which famous person do you admire?
    Would you mind telling me _____?
3   Do you consider yourself successful?
    Could you tell me _____?
4   Who is the most talented person in your family?
    I'd like to know _____.
5   Has she ever received an award?
    Do you know _____?

7 Complete the questions about high achievers in different fields.

→ **STUDY TIP** First find out which are subject questions and which are object questions.

1   François Englert and Peter Higgs received a Nobel prize in 2013 for a particle they had discovered nearly fifty years before.
    a   Who _received a Nobel prize_ in 2013?
    b   When _did Englert and Higgs receive_ a Nobel prize?
2   Sixteen-year-old Malala Yousafzai received the United Nations Human Rights Award in 2013.
    a   Who _____ in 2013?
    b   What _____ in 2013?
3   The Brazilian writer Paulo Coelho has sold over 150 million books in more than 150 countries.
    a   Who _____ in more than 150 countries?
    b   How many _____ sold?
4   Usain Bolt won three gold medals in the 2012 Olympic Games.
    a   Who _____ in the 2012 Olympic Games?
    b   In which Olympic Games _____ three gold medals?
5   Chinese businessman Liu Qiangdong became a billionaire before he was forty.
    a   Which Chinese businessman _____ before he was forty?
    b   What _____ before he was forty?

I can …	Very well	Quite well	More practice
talk about experts and high achievers.	○	○	○
make and answer indirect and subject and object questions.	○	○	○

7.3 Vocabulary development

Vocabulary collocations

1 Match 1–8 to a–h to form collocations.

1	got	a	progress
2	completely	b	risks
3	came up with	c	jobs
4	think	d	different
5	did	e	promoted
6	make	f	creatively
7	temporary	g	the idea
8	take	h	his best

2 Complete the sentences with collocations from exercise **1**.

1 J. K. Rowling is now very successful, but her life before *Harry Potter* was _completely different_. She _____ for her magical world while she was poor, divorced and depressed.

2 Before becoming the film character Indiana Jones, Harrison Ford didn't _____ in his career as an actor for ten years. He had to do several _____, including working as a carpenter.

3 Steve Jobs always liked to _____, but he was fired from his own company when he failed. He returned to Apple in 1997 and _____ to president of the company in 2000.

4 Inventors have to _____, but they also have to be persistent. Even though he always _____, Thomas Edison failed thousands of times before inventing the light bulb.

3 Complete the article with words from the box.

best   completely   following   get   higher   hugely   ~~job~~   obey   satisfaction
supervise   take

Learning from failure

Have you missed that really good [1] _job_ opportunity you prepared for so much? Have you done your [2]_____ but still didn't [3]_____ promoted? Well, failing is part of everybody's life, so here are some tips for you to deal better with failure.

Don't make it personal.   Even if a [4]_____ important project was a failure, that doesn't mean that *you* are. These are [5]_____ different things, and mixing them up can destroy your confidence.

Don't think too much about it.   Have a 24-hour rule. Allow yourself a day to celebrate success or feel bad about failure. Then get back to work. If you always [6]_____ this rule, you will learn from your mistakes but won't let them damage your job [7]_____.

Try a new point of view.   Most big ideas don't come from [8]_____ procedures. Try to see the problem in different ways and don't be afraid to [9]_____ risks!

Don't point fingers.   If you [10]_____ employees or are in a [11]_____ position in the company, it is easy to blame those below you. Have an honest discussion with your team to find out what went wrong.

Vocabulary review

4 Complete the words in the table.

Working conditions	High achievers
career pros_ _ _ _ _ _ s	ach_ _ _ _ _ _ fame
hol_ _ _ _ _ _ pay	achie_ _ _ _ _ents
job satis_ _ _ _ _ _ _ _ _	amb_ _ _ _ _ _ _ _
make someone redun_ _ _ _ _ _	aw_ _ _ds
promo_ _ _ _ _ _	cham_ _ _ _ _n
qualif_ _ _ _ _ _ _ _ _ s	determ_ _ _ _d
occupa_ _ _ _ _	ex_ _ _ _ _ _
rent-free accom_ _ _ _ _ _ _ _ _ _ _	famous
sala_ _ _	hard-w_ _ _ _ing
s_ _ _ _ _ pay	tal_ _ _ted
unem_ _ _ _ _ed	well-k_ _ _ _ _ _
wo_ _ _ _ _ _ hours	

7.4   Speaking and writing

<table>
<tr>
<td>

Speaking clarification

1 **7.5** 》 James applied for a job and was called back for a second interview. Listen and choose the correct options.

  1 He was offered *the job he had applied for / a different job.*

  2 The company has had *a good relationship with journalists recently / problems with journalists recently.*

  3 He *took the job / wasn't interested in the job.*

2a **7.5** 》 Match 1–4 to a–d. Then listen again and check.

  1 I'm not sure   a you're offering me another job?

  2 Do you mean   b think …

  3 Well, for   c I understand.

  4 Let me   d instance, press conferences.

  b Which of the phrases can we use to …

  • ask for clarification? _1_ and ___

  • get time to think? ___

  • give clarification? ___

3a **7.6** 》 Complete the conversations from James's first day at work with one suitable word in each space. Then listen and check.

  Conversation 1

  James   I'm afraid Mr Clarkson is not available any more, but I'm in charge of PR now, and I'm happy to answer your questions.

  Journalist 'Not available'? Could you explain ¹_____ you ²_____? Is this related to the recent scandal?

  James   No, it isn't. He doesn't work here any longer, but I'm afraid I can't comment on the reasons. Next question!

  Conversation 2

  James OK, so now I've met all of you, I'd like to talk about our image. I think we need something new and fresh. Any suggestions?

  Marie I'm not ³_____ I understand …

  James Let me ⁴_____ you an example … OK, ⁵_____ me think … Right. This logo. How long have you had this logo?

  b Which conversation is part of a …

  • meeting? ___   • press conference? ___

</td>
<td>

Writing an application letter or email

4 Complete the phrases with one suitable word.

  1 my m*ain* responsibility is …

  2 As you will see in the a_____ CV …

  3 I w_____ be happy to …

  4 I would like the o_____ to work …

  5 I look f_____ to hearing from you.

  6 If you need f_____ information …

  7 I am writing r_____ the position of …

5 Complete the email with phrases from exercise 4.

☒

Dear Sir or Madam,

ᵃ_7_ Assistant Marketing Manager advertised in the magazine *The Market* this month.

ᵇ___, I am currently working in the marketing department of an online clothes store. In my present position, ᶜ___ creating advertisements for social media. I have also worked in the public relations department for the city council, dealing with the press and customer complaints.

I have strong interpersonal skills and work well under pressure. ᵈ___ for your company because I believe I could use my skills to further develop the solid reputation of your company.

ᵉ___ attend an interview, and I would be able to start work next month. ᶠ___, please contact me on 01724 6290929, or email me at jstevenson@dmail.com.

ᵍ___

Yours faithfully,

James Stevenson

</td>
</tr>
</table>

I can …	Very well	Quite well	More practice
understand and use collocations on creative thinking.	○	○	○
ask for and give clarification.	○	○	○
write an application letter or email.	○	○	○

8.1   World happiness report

Vocabulary   happiness factors

1   Complete each point with one word from each box.

A   balanced   ~~cultural~~   health   high   leisure   physical   strong

B   activity   ~~activities~~   care   diet   economy   taxes   time

People are generally happier when …

- they have enough time and money for [1] *cultural activities* , such as going to the cinema.
- they don't have to work very long hours and so have enough [2]_____ _____.
- they can afford a [3]_____ _____, which includes the right combination of vitamins, proteins and carbohydrates.
- they pay [4]_____ _____, and as a result their country offers good quality services, such as free [5]_____.
- their country has a [6]_____ _____, without high inflation or frequent financial crises.
- they do enough [7]_____ _____, such as walking, swimming or team sports.

2a   Complete the answers to the survey with one suitable word in each gap. The first letter is given.

What has made you especially happy or unhappy recently?

1   'I was really pleased when my company started to offer *childcare* . It really changed my life because now I can spend much more time with my son.'

2   'I know this sounds awful, but it was when my n_____ moved out last month! He was so noisy and the walls are really thin.'

3   'I've only been living in the capital for three months, and it's been really hard to get used to the p_____. My eyes really burn sometimes.'

4   'I watched a documentary on global p_____ last week. It really breaks your heart to see that so many have so little.'

5   'During my holiday, I worked for two weeks as a v_____ in an old people's home. The old people were fantastic and I learnt so much from them.'

b   **8.1**))) Listen and check.

c   Which people mentioned events that made them …
- happy? _1_ , ___ and ___
- unhappy? ___ , ___ and ___

➔ **STUDY TIP** Make a list of collocations like *balanced diet* and *leisure activity* and record them in your vocabulary notebook with an example sentence.

3 Complete the text from the magazine article below with words from the box.

activities	economy	~~healthcare~~
leisure	neighbours	physical
pollution	volunteer

THE SIX SECRETS OF HAPPINESS

National issues such as ¹ _healthcare_ , how strong the ² _____ is and the level of ³ _____ in the air can make a big difference to your general happiness. However, researchers have found that there are six important factors in your personal life which can make you much happier:

- **Having strong relationships**
  Happy people not only have good friends and a loving family but also get on well with colleagues and ⁴ _____.

- **Doing things you are good at**
  The satisfaction of doing something well, such as a sport or other ⁵ _____ activities, contributes a lot to your happiness.

- **Not staying in a job you hate**
  Remember, you're going to spend around 2,000 hours a year doing it, so make sure you like what you do.

- **Planning your happiness**
  Include cultural ⁶ _____ and arrangements with people you like in your calendar.

- **Doing things that really mean something to you**
  It's fine to have fun in your ⁷ _____ time, but you should also find something that brings a deeper sense of achievement.

- **Doing ⁸ _____ work (but not too often!)**
  Helping others makes you happier, but researchers say you can feel stressed if you do too much.

Grammar real conditionals

4 Choose the best options to complete the text.

The Happiest Man on Earth

'If you can learn how to ride a bike, you ¹*learn* / *can learn* how to be happy,' says 67-year-old French monk Matthieu Ricard. After detailed brain scans, he was considered by scientists to be the happiest man in the world. We interviewed him to find out what he can teach us.

The first thing he recommends is to understand your feelings. If you ²*feel* / *will feel* angry, you may lose control of yourself. But if you start to understand what you are feeling, you will be able to control your anger in a short time. You ³*will be* / *won't be* completely happy unless you ⁴*will get rid* / *can get rid* of bad feelings.

According to Matthieu, the best way to control your feelings is by doing meditation. If you ⁵*meditate* / *will meditate* for twenty minutes a day, you deal better with everything else during the other twenty-three hours and forty minutes. You don't need to have a lot of experience, either. If you ⁶*start* / *will start* meditating today, you will see the results in a month.

A last piece of advice? Anyone ⁷*is* / *can be* the happiest person in the world if they ⁸*look* / *will look* in the right place. So, find out what happiness really is for you and go for it!

PRONUNCIATION intonation

5a **8.2**〉) Listen to the two conditional sentences and choose the correct words in italics to complete the rule.

If you meditate, you'll feel happy.

You'll feel happy if you meditate.

In conditional sentences, the intonation usually rises in the *first / second* part and falls in the *first / second*.

b **8.3**〉) Listen to these parts from famous quotes about happiness and write (1) if they are the first part of the sentence or (2) if they are the second.

a if you want happiness for a lifetime _1_
b you will be successful ___
c you'll never enjoy the sunshine ___
d if you can't love and respect yourself ___
e you are too busy ___
f you will never be happy ___

c **8.4**〉) Listen to the whole quotes and check.

d **8.4**〉) Look at the audioscript on page 93. Listen again and repeat.

I can …	Very well	Quite well	More practice
talk about quality of life.	○	○	○
talk about real conditions.	○	○	○

8.2 What makes a hero?

1 Choose the two adjectives that describe the people who performed these real-life good deeds.

a Teacher Rajesh Sharma gives free lessons to poor children under a bridge in India.
embarrassed / educated / kind

b Fourteen-year-old Marcos Ugarte saved a child from a burning building. *brave / selfish / heroic*

c Glen James, who was homeless, found a backpack with $42,000 in it, and gave it to the police.
honest / calm / responsible

d Allen and Violet Large won $10.9 million in the lottery and donated 98% of it to charity.
lucky / generous / ordinary

e Seven-year-old Diego Pimentel didn't panic and called the emergency number when his babysitter had a serious epileptic fit. *calm / crazy / responsible*

f *Star Wars* fans all over the world are raising money to help a baby called 'Princess Leia', who has a mystery illness. *kind / afraid / generous*

2 Complete the forum with words from the box.

afraid   calm   crazy   embarrassed   ordinary   ~~selfish~~

☒

Topic: Heroes

suzy23: What jobs do you consider heroic?

catlover: I think it depends. Even the most ¹ *selfish* person is capable of being a hero in some circumstances.

jessicasw: Mums! I used to be ² _____ by mine, but now I'm older I know she's a real hero!

tokyo_girl7: 'Someone can display courage by doing the out-of-the-ordinary, another by doing the ³ _____.' Søren Kierkegaard

rstewart: In my opinion, anyone who feels ⁴ _____ and still acts is a hero.

skate4ever: I really admire people who can stay ⁵ _____ in dangerous situations, like people who do extreme sports.

caleb45: Sorry, skate4ever, but I don't agree with you. I think these people are just ⁶ _____. Real heroes, like fire-fighters or policemen, risk their lives to help other people.

---

3 Choose the best words to complete the article.

Four great heroes of the big screen (and the biggest villain!)

Who doesn't love a hero? Well, not everybody … Some people are not ¹*embarrassed / calm* to confess they prefer the bad guy! Here are four heroes and a villain:

James Bond This ²*ordinary / heroic* secret agent is always ³*afraid / calm* and charming, even in end-of-world situations.

Severus Snape All the students were ⁴*afraid / brave* of this strict teacher, but in the end he was a hero.

Erin Brockovich Julia Roberts plays an ⁵*ordinary / selfish* woman who fights against a big corporation.

Sanjuro Tsubaki The samurai played by Toshiro Mifune is an example of the ⁶*lucky / brave* warrior who is always ⁷*honest / embarrassed*, no matter the cost.

Hannibal Lecter Forget the dark Darth Vader or the ⁸*crazy / responsible* Joker in *Batman*. The worst villain of all movies, according to the American Film Institute, is this highly ⁹*heroic / educated*, psychopathic psychiatrist from *The Silence of the Lambs*.

Grammar unreal conditionals

4   Choose the correct form of the verbs to complete the test.

How brave are you?
Take the test and find out!

- If you ¹(saw) / *would see* someone   **Yes / No**
stealing from a shop, ²*did / would* you
tell the shop assistant?

- If someone you didn't like from work   **Yes / No**
³*got / would get* fired because of a
mistake you made, ⁴*did / would* you
tell the boss?

- ⁵*Did / Would* you do a parachute   **Yes / No**
jump if someone ⁶*gave / would give*
you £1,000 to do it?

- If an animal ⁷*was / would be* in   **Yes / No**
danger, ⁸*did / would* you risk your
own life to save it?

5a   Complete Sonya's conversation with Li about the test
above with the correct form of the verbs in brackets.

S   The first one's easy. I ¹*'d definitely tell* (definitely/tell)
the shop assistant.

L   Me, too. It actually happened to me once. Hmm ...
What's next? I think I ² _____
(confess) my mistake to my boss, even if I hated the guy.

S   I don't know, that's a hard one. But this one's not:
I ³ _____ (never/do) a parachute
jump, even if they ⁴ _____ (give) me
£1,000,000!

L   Really? Well, I ⁵ _____ (jump) today if
I ⁶ _____ (have) the chance. And for
free!

S   Not for me, thanks! What about this one, about the
animal? What ⁷ _____ (you/do)?

L   I have to admit I ⁸ _____ (not risk) my
life, unless it ⁹ _____ (be) my own pet.

S   I guess, but I think I ¹⁰ _____ (try) to
save any animal if I ¹¹ _____ (not have)
to risk my own life.

L   Well, I suppose we haven't done too badly, have we?

b   **8.5** ❱❱ Listen and check.

6   Correct the mistakes in the answers people gave to the poll
question below.

In which situation would you help a complete stranger?

1   If a disabled person ~~needs~~ *needed* to
cross a street, I would help
them.

2   I would stop my car,
if someone needed
help on a highway at
night.

3   I might give blood
unless the local
hospital needed it.

4   I carried an elderly
woman's shopping
to her house, even if
it wasn't near mine.

5   If I would call an
ambulance if I saw a
cyclist hit by a car.

6   I would help strangers if I
might, but I'm usually in a hurry.

7   Complete the second sentences in 1–6 so they have a
similar meaning to the first sentences. Use the words in
brackets.

1   I'm too old to be a policeman. (if)
I would be a policeman *if I were younger* .

2   I think you should do something about it. (were)
If _____ do something about it.

3   I can't help because I don't know first aid. (would)
I _____ first aid.

4   We aren't generous because we don't have enough
money. (if)
We _____ had more money.

5   It's possible that I'd do something if I saw a parent
shouting at a child. (might)
I _____ I saw a parent shouting at a
child.

6   People don't help more because there aren't enough
charity campaigns on TV. (more)
People would help more _____
charity campaigns on TV.

I can ...	Very well	Quite well	More practice
talk about personality and behaviour.	○	○	○
talk about unreal situations in the present and future.	○	○	○

8.3 Vocabulary development

Vocabulary prefixes

1 Match the correct prefix in box A to each word in box B.

A | mis- re- in- over-

B | appear behave eat convenient judge formal new spend understand

2 Use the correct form of the words from exercise **1** to complete the sentences.

1 I have to _renew_ my passport before we go abroad next month.

2 It's difficult not to _____ at this time of the year as there are so many parties. I know I've put on weight.

3 In the countries I visit, I hardly ever see children _____. They are usually so good!

4 I am very sorry if the meeting on Friday is _____ for you, but it is the only day the rest of the group can manage.

5 Just when I thought we'd never see our cat again, he _____ looking a bit hungry, but otherwise fine.

6 No, I didn't _____. You didn't say 11 o'clock. You said 12, I'm sure of it.

7 Fortunately, you won't have to dress up. It's a very _____ party.

8 You know, people have _____ him. He isn't lazy or dishonest. He's incredibly hard-working and he never lies.

9 This is all the money you are going to receive this month. Make sure you don't _____.

3 Choose the correct words to complete the sentences.

1 *Inactive / Overactive* people are more likely to have health problems than people who do a lot of exercise.

2 I'd like to *rearrange / replace* the meeting on Thursday, please. Could you make it Friday?

3 Honestly, I think you're *overacting / overreacting*. There is no need to get so angry.

4 These prices are *incorrect / overpriced*. Everything has gone up by 10%. Please change them.

5 I can't believe they've *misplaced / misspelled* my name again. It's got one 's', not two.

6 They had to cancel the ceremony at the last minute. Have they *renewed / rescheduled* it yet?

4 Replace the phrases in italics with one word with an appropriate prefix.

1 The taxi driver must have *understood wrongly* [*misunderstood*] what I said.

2 I'll have to go to Hong Kong tomorrow. Could you *arrange my schedule again*?

3 Oh, dear! The children have been *behaving badly* again.

4 I'm really sorry I broke your Moroccan lamp, I know I can't *put a new one in place of* it.

5 I'm not surprised you haven't got any money at the moment. You *spent far too much* last month.

Vocabulary review

5 Complete the lists with words from the box.

afraid ~~balanced diet~~ generous healthcare kind physical activity pollution selfish

Factors for and against happiness

Individual	Society
1 _balanced diet_	childcare
cultural activities	3 _____
leisure time	high taxes
neighbours	4 _____
2 _____	poverty
volunteer	strong economy

Personality and behaviour

Positive	Negative
brave	7 _____
calm	crazy
educated	embarrassed
5 _____	ordinary
heroic	8 _____
honest	
6 _____	
lucky	
responsible	

8.4　Speaking and writing

Speaking　giving a talk

1　**8.6**))) Listen to extracts A–D and match them to problems 1–4.

1　Talking too fast ___
2　Not practised for the talk _A_
3　Reading from notes ___
4　Boring, flat intonation ___

2a　**8.7**))) Listen to the improved versions of extracts A–D from exercise **1**. Which part of the talk are they from?

Introduction: _A_ and ___　　Main body: ___　Conclusion: ___

b　Complete the phrases with one word in each gap.

1　_Firstly_ , I'm going to explain why there are so many distractions around us.
2　_____, I'm going to tell you about the three main distractions we have to deal with, ...
3　also and _____ I'm ... going to suggest ways of staying focused.
4　So we've _____ at the main distractions around us, ...
5　Now I'd like to _____ with a phrase from an American golfer ...
6　... my name's Rashid and I'm going to _____ about choices.
7　Let's move _____ now to look at ...
8　... the third and _____ thing you can do to deal with choices.

c　**8.7**))) Listen again and check.

Writing　taking notes

3　Match abbreviations 1–9 to words a–i.

1	conn	a	distractions
2	curts	b	focused
3	distr	c	urgent
4	foc	d	connected
5	h/day	e	hours a day
6	mob	f	curtains
7	ppl	g	mobile
8	prof	h	professional
9	urgt	i	people

4　**8.8**))) Listen and complete the notes with abbreviations from exercise **3**.

DISTRACTIONS

Intro:
• Why so many?
• 3 main ¹ _distr_
• ways of staying ² _____

Main body:
Everything ³ _____ –
⁴ _____ 24 ⁵ _____ →
disaster work / studies

1　⁶ _____ around you: talk later
2　Outside noises: put up ⁷ _____
3　Alerts on ⁸ _____: turn off. sound!

Conc:
⁹ _____ golfer Tom Kite: 'You'll always find a distraction if you're looking for one.'

I can ...	Very well	Quite well	More practice
use prefixes.	○	○	○
give a talk.	○	○	○
make notes.	○	○	○

8.5 Listening for pleasure

Eating for free

1 Match the phrases in the box to the photos.

   a   bartering for food with friends
   b   collecting seaweed
   c   foraging for mushrooms
   d   growing your own produce
   e   picking berries
   f   taking waste food from a supermarket

2 **8.9** 》 Listen to an interview with Danny Clarke (D), a man who believes in eating for free.

3 Complete the paragraph with the correct form of the verbs in the box.

> barter ~~buy~~ collect forage grow save spend waste

If, instead of ^{1} _buying_ food, we ^{2}_____ more time ^{3}_____ fruit and vegetables in our gardens, we would appreciate our food more. Similarly, if we ^{4}_____ for food in woodlands or on beaches, ^{5}_____ wild plants, for example, or seaweed, we ^{6}_____ money, which we could spend on other things. It's terrible that we ^{7}_____ so much food – we throw it away even when we could eat it! If we ^{8}_____ for goods with friends, and shared our produce with each other, we would be more self-sufficient and much happier.

4 Would you consider trying any of the ways of eating for free that Danny suggests? Why/Why not? What other ways of getting free food can you think of?

Review: Units 7 and 8

Grammar

1 Complete the article below with one word in each gap.

What makes people happy?

Professor Ruut Veenhoven, from Erasmus University in the Netherlands, studied data about happiness from around the world and came to these conclusions:

- People feel happier if they **1** _are_ in a long-term relationship and have close friendships.
- If you start going out for dinner more, you **2**_____ feel better than you do now.
- You might **3**_____ happier if you think you are good-looking (even if you aren't!).
- Good jobs make people happy **4**_____ they have to travel more than an hour to get to work. Most people said they **5**_____ be happier if they worked near their homes.
- When you have children, you feel less happy than you used **6**_____ be. But when they grow up and leave home, you feel happier than before!

Professor Veenhoven has been asking people **7**_____ they are happy and encouraging them to keep a diary to find out what makes them feel good. One of these people, Jana Koopman, says the diary changed her life. She now does activities she didn't **8**_____ to do, like painting, and she also realized she **9**_____ to worry too much about cleaning!

Vocabulary

2 Complete the sentences. Use words from the box.

childcare economy ~~healthcare~~ holiday leisure
salary satisfaction working

Which is the best country to live in? The OECD (Organization for Economic Co-operation and Development) made a list based on issues such as **1** _healthcare_ , education and job **2**_____. Here are some serious candidates:

- **Canada** The average **3**_____ hours there are around thirty per week, lower than most countries.
- **Norway** They take **4**_____ very seriously in this European country. Mothers can stay at home for up to forty-seven weeks taking care of their babies, while still receiving a full **5**_____.
- **France** French workers have a lot of **6**_____ time: they get thirty days' paid **7**_____, and they also have ten national holidays during the year.

- **Australia** A strong **8**_____ and excellent services put this country at the top of OECD's list in terms of quality of life.

3 Choose the best words to complete the text about heroism.

The hero in all of us

What do most **1**(well-known)/ ambitious heroes from films and books have in common? Joseph Campbell, in his book *The Hero with a Thousand Faces*, describes a cycle, called the Hero's Journey. There are several steps in this journey to a special world: heroes receive help from an **2**award / expert, go through difficulties, show how **3**brave / ordinary and **4**selfish / determined they are when fighting their worst enemy, receive some sort of **5**achievement / award for that and finally go back to their normal life, but now as a hero.

And what do we, **6**ordinary / famous people, have in common with these **7**heroic / lucky characters? Well, we may not have to kill dragons or perform dangerous tasks, but we go through the same cycle in different moments of our lives. We leave our comfort zone (our normal daily routine), go through experiences that transform us (such as a personal crisis or a training course we do), and come out a better person, more **8**afraid / responsible or **9**embarrassed / generous, for example.

Learn to identify these opportunities in your life, and don't be **10**afraid / crazy of the journey!

Speaking

4a Complete each sentence by adding the word in brackets in the correct position.

1 Let's move ᴼⁿ̖ now to talk about the effects of social media. (on)
2 I'm to talk to you about decisions. (here)
3 Could you give some examples of your achievements? (me)
4 So we've looked ̖ the main factors that create stress. (at)
5 What I is that I have good time management skills. (mean)
6 Well, instance, I designed my last company's social networking page. (for)

b Which of these phrases would you hear in a ...

- talk? _1_ , ___ and ___
- job interview? ___ , ___ and ___

Appearances

9.1 Real beauty?

describing physical appearance

1 Complete the descriptions of three famous scientists with words from the box. There are four words you do not need.

> bald   curly   dyed   eyelashes   ~~face~~   forehead   fringe
> jaw   moustache   spiky   stubble

Great Scientists in the National Portrait Gallery in London

Have you ever wondered what famous people from history really looked like? Well, take a walk around London's National Portrait Gallery and you'll get to meet all of Britain's greats.

On my last visit, I saw Godfrey Kneller's 1702 portrait of **Isaac Newton**, the man who discovered the law of gravity. He had a long ¹ _face_ , a large ² _____ and a very large ³ _____, which is not surprising when you consider how brilliant the brain behind that part of his body was.

I also saw Thomas Phillips' 1842 portrait of **Michael Faraday**, the scientist who discovered how to use electricity. Like Newton, he had very ⁴ _____ hair, and he was clean-shaven, so he didn't have any ⁵ _____ on his chin. In contrast, **Ernest Rutherford**, the man who first split the atom in 1917, had the most wonderful ⁶ _____. It was so large you couldn't see the top of his mouth! And his hair was brushed to one side, perhaps to hide the fact that he was going ⁷ _____.

2 Match the sentence halves.
1 Terry is an extremely well-_c_
2 Pedro has been clean-___
3 Amy is a little bit overweight, ___
4 Luc is middle-___
5 Laila has shoulder-___

a so she's about to start a diet.
b length hair, which she wears in a ponytail.
c built man who goes to the gym every day.
d shaven ever since he got rid of his beard.
e aged but still wears tight jeans.

3 Choose the correct adjectives to complete the descriptions made to a police artist.
1 The thief had dyed, blonde hair and amazing, (long) / slim / round eyelashes.
2 The burglar wasn't fat at all. She was tall and *thick / slim / double* and she looked quite young, *in her twenty / in her twenties / in twenties*, I think.
3 The person I saw had a *spiky / dyed / round* face, shaped like the full moon, and a *double / slim / bald* chin. He was fat, and not in *round / good / large* shape at all.
4 He looked very unusual. He had a *round / large / double* jaw which stuck out from his face, and *thick / spiky / slim* eyebrows, which he really needed to cut with a pair of scissors.
5 She was an *elder / elderly / middle-aged* lady – over seventy, I'd say – and she wasn't exactly fat, but she was *a little thick / overweight / well-built*.

Grammar comparison

4 Complete the sentences with words from the box.

> as bit isn't less most ~~more~~ much than

1 Tom's a lot _more_ hard-working than I thought he was.
2 Amelia is slimmer _____ both her sisters.
3 Jaime _____ as strong as he looks.
4 Oleg is _____ cleverer than the rest of us.
5 Unfortunately, I'm far _____ talented than my older brother.
6 Penny's hair is as blonde _____ mine.
7 Amir's a _____ more independent now.
8 Gabriel is the _____ fascinating man I know.

5 Complete the sentences with the correct comparative or superlative form of the words in brackets.

1 Although much _slimmer_ (slim) now than he was, Mauricio is still on a diet.
2 Hollywood actor George Clooney seems to be regularly voted the _____ (attractive) man in the world.
3 Tonya is a lot _____ (interested) in painting than her brother. She loves art.
4 My hair isn't any _____ (curly) than Jo's.
5 Ivan is underweight, but Sergei is even _____ (thin). He really needs to eat more.
6 Eduardo is the _____ (vain) man I know! He's always looking in the mirror.

6 Put the words in order to make comparative or superlative sentences.

1 I thought / was / less / would be / supportive / a lot / she / Maria / than .
  Maria was _a lot less supportive than I thought she would be._
2 I know / is / the / insecure / Luke / person / most .
  Luke _____
3 his brother, / more / Mohsen / than / confident / is / Kamal / far .
  Mohsen _____
4 than / used / much / My hair / now / shorter / it is / to be .
  My hair _____
5 valuable / in / most / is / the museum / This / the / painting .
  This _____

7 Complete the text with the comparative or superlative form of the words in brackets.

Are men vain?

OK, it's true. I am vain. I'm a 35-year-old man, but most people think I'm [1] _much older_ (much/old), and I'll do anything to look [2]_____ (as/young) I once did. My wife is [3]_____ (far/worried) I am about the ageing process. She doesn't seem concerned at all, in fact. That's probably why she was [4]_____ (even/surprised) I expected when I came home last month with a new, smooth forehead. 'Have you had Botox?' she asked, her mouth open [5]_____ (as/wide) the Channel Tunnel. I had to say yes. 'Having Botox injections is [6]_____ (no/unusual) getting your hair cut,' I argued. 'And it makes me feel [7]_____ (lot/good) about myself.' She just smiled. It's impossible to argue with someone [8]_____ (as/vain) me. And I'm not alone. Did you know that in the UK, the cosmetics market for men is growing twice [9]_____ (as/fast) the women's market? Worldwide, the market is worth about £20 billion, and that's why for cosmetics companies, it's by far [10]_____ (exciting) time ever to produce new men's products. Watch out! A new age of male vanity has begun.

I can …	Very well	Quite well	More practice
describe appearances.	○	○	○
make comparisons.	○	○	○

9.2 Paintings

Vocabulary describing paintings

1 Complete the categories with the words in the box.

> curves   modern   old-fashioned   seems   ~~soft~~
> tells a story   traditional   warm

Adjectives that describe colours
colourful   **1** _____*soft*_____
bright   **2** _____

Adjectives that describe age and style
historical   **4** _____
mysterious   **5** _____
3 _____

Verbs and verb phrases to describe a picture
looks   **7** _____
6 _____

Nouns to describe line and shape
straight lines   **8** _____

2 Match words from exercise **1** to the extracts from art reviews below.

1   This fifteenth-century painting is important because it tells us what was happening in Milan at the time ... (adjective) _*historical*_

2   Pollock's work uses oranges, reds, blues, greens, dark browns ... just about everything in fact! (adjective) _____

3   In this painting, we find out what happened after Peter left Rome and ... (verb phrase) _____

4   Although painted in 1990, it doesn't look modern at all – it already looks out of date ... (adjective) _____

5   He uses the feminine shapes of bridges and rainbows in his art ... (noun) _____

6   We really don't know why the artist painted this, or what it means ... (adjective) _____

PRONUNCIATION Stress

3a **9.1**))) Listen and circle the stressed syllable in each word.

1   historical   4   mysterious   7   old-fashioned
2   colourful   5   modern
3   detailed   6   traditional

b **9.1**))) Listen again. Pause the listening and repeat after each word.

4 Complete the review with words and phrases from the box.

> the background   the bottom right-hand corner   the left
> the middle of   front of   the foreground

Las Meninas Painted in 1656 by the Spanish artist Diego Velázquez, this famous painting shows the Spanish king's little daughter visiting the artist's studio. She is standing in **1**_____ the painting, in **2**_____, and she is looking at us directly. A big dog is lying in **3**_____ of the picture. On **4**_____, the artist has painted himself in **5**_____ a very large canvas. Interestingly, even though we can't see what's on the canvas, we know what Velázquez is painting because there is a mirror in **6**_____ showing the king and queen's reflection. This painting makes you ask many questions, and the more you look at it, the more complex it becomes. It is a portrait of the princess, a portrait of life at court, a portrait of the king and queen and a self-portrait of the artist at work! Or is it really a painting about painting?

→ **STUDY TIP** Notice the use of *in*, *at* and *on/to* when describing a picture. We say *at the top* or *at the bottom*, *on/to the left* or *on/to the right*, but *in the middle*, *in front* and *in the corner*, and *in the foreground* or *background*.

Grammar deduction and speculation

5a Edith has a painting, not a poster, on the wall of her room. Read what her friends say about it on a social networking site, and choose the best modal verbs to complete the sentences.

VICTOR Did anyone else see that painting on Edith's wall at the party at her house last Saturday? I think it's real. If so, she ¹(must)/ could / can't be a secret millionaire!

TOMAS Don't be stupid! It ²must / might / can't be real! It's a famous painting by Turner. The original is in a museum in London!

VICTOR Oh, right. But what reason ³must / could / can't she have for hanging a painting like that in her room?

PENNY Lots of reasons. The painting ⁴must / could / can't have a special significance, for example. Edith's English. Who knows? Turner ⁵must / might / can't be her great-grandfather.

TOMAS Unlikely, Penny. LOL.

PENNY OK, but it ⁶must / could / can't be there by accident. Everybody chooses pictures for a reason, and that includes Edith.

EDITH What are you guys talking about? You ⁷must / might / can't be really bored if this is all you have to chat about! The painting was there when I moved in, it's fixed to the wall, and the landlord told me not to move it! I suspect I know why, too. There ⁸must / might / can't be a really big hole in the wall behind it!

b **9.2**)) Listen and check your answers to exercise **5a**. Notice the strong stress on *must, might, could* and *can't*. Listen and repeat.

6 Complete the text with *must, might* or *can't.*

The Lost Leonardo?

In Palazzo Vecchio in Florence, there is a large sixteenth-century painting that covers one of the walls. It ¹ _must_ be over ten metres wide – at least! And it's by the artist Giorgio Vasari, who was a fine painter, but one you ² _____ not know. 'It's a great painting,' says one well-known art expert, 'but we think there ³ _____ be an even greater painting behind it. We aren't sure, of course, but we now have the technology to look closer. Who knows what we ⁴ _____ find.'

Historical records show that there was a large painting by Leonardo da Vinci in the Palazzo Vecchio when Vasari started painting. But where is it now? Many experts don't believe that Vasari would have destroyed Leonardo's work, so it ⁵ _____ be lost forever. It's just hidden. In the corner of his own painting, Vasari wrote *cerca trova* (look and you will find), which ⁶ _____ be a clue. It's a possibility that has excited many in the art world. '*Cerca trova* ⁷ _____ mean something!' says one expert. 'Vasari wrote it for a reason. We ⁸ _____ be certain, of course, but we think it ⁹ _____ mean that the lost Leonardo is behind Vasari's painting. And, if it is, it ¹⁰ _____ be Leonardo's largest surviving painting. He painted nothing else so big.'

I can ...	Very well	Quite well	More practice
describe a scene.	○	○	○
speculate and make deductions.	○	○	○

9.3 Vocabulary development

Vocabulary phrasal verbs

1 Correct the incorrect sentences by rewriting the part in italics. If the sentence is correct, put a tick.

1 One day, scientists will *come up with a cure* for cancer.
   ✓

2 Can I leave the kids with you while I go to the shop? You don't mind *looking them after*, do you?
   looking after them

3 You've missed the flight. The plane has already *taken off it.* _____

4 The party should be great. I'm really *looking forward to it.* _____

5 You need to decide what course to take. Have you *thought your choices about?* _____

6 The photo isn't clear, but I think that's Nick. I can just *make out him* in the background.
   _____

7 The vacuum cleaner doesn't work. It has *broken it down.* _____

8 We need to decorate the walls. I'm thinking of *putting some posters up.* _____

2 Complete the phrasal verbs with the correct particle from the box. You can use the particles more than once.

   across   after   off   on   round   up

1 Why don't you come _round_ on Sunday? We'll have a barbecue.

2 Shelley has taken _____ tae kwon do. It's a martial art and she really enjoys doing it.

3 Andy hates decorating – that's why he keeps putting _____ repainting the bedroom. He'll have to do it one day.

4 Patrizia takes _____ her mother. They are both very generous and sociable people.

5 I've never really got _____ with Pavel. We're just very different people.

6 Toni has given _____ studying for her music exams. They were just too hard and she'd rather do something else.

7 I tried to look the word _____ in the dictionary, but I couldn't find it.

8 I came _____ these old photos when I was cleaning the attic.

Vocabulary review

3 Match words a–j to what they can be used to describe (1–10).

a detailed   historical   old-fashioned   traditional
b double chin   round face   large jaw/forehead
c fringe   going bald   grey
d seems   tells a story   looks
e blonde   curly   dyed   spiky
f bright   soft   warm
g in good shape   overweight   well-built   slim
h middle-aged   elderly
i long eyelashes   stubble   thick eyebrows clean-shaven   moustache
j colourful   modern   mysterious

1 colours in a painting _f_
2 faces ____
3 new abstract paintings ____
4 women's hair (usually) ____
5 men's hair (usually) ____
6 old realistic paintings ____
7 verbs to describe paintings ____
8 people's sizes ____
9 people's ages ____
10 facial hair ____

4 Circle the word, a or b, that completes sentences 1–6.

1 This painting looks _____.
   a a story   b old-fashioned

2 He's going _____.
   a bald   b blonde

3 He's got stubble on his _____.
   a chin   b eyelashes

4 The abstract painting is made up of straight _____.
   a lines   b curves

5 Tom's hair? I'd say it's shoulder-_____.
   a width   b length

6 Harry has a very round_____.
   a face   b moustache

9.4   Speaking and writing

Speaking making complaints

1a **9.3**))) Greg has noisy neighbours. Listen to him making a complaint. Tick the two problems that are mentioned.

1 dog barking ___
2 baby crying ___
3 alarm going off ___
4 speakers booming ___

b **9.3**))) Complete the extracts from the conversation. Then listen again and check.

1 Sorry to bother you, but there's _____ I'm not happy about.
2 ... I'm sorry _____ that.
3 _____ the problem?
4 I_____ that it _____ mean ...
5 The _____'s been going _____ for weeks.
6 _____ are we supposed to do _____ it?
7 But maybe you _____ move ...
8 I'll make _____ I turn the volume _____.
9 _____ you think you could do _____ about the noise?

PRONUNCIATION sentence stress

2a **9.4**))) Listen to extracts from conversations between neighbours. Underline the main stress in each extract.

1 Do you think you could turn your music down?
2 Your dog's barking keeps waking me up.
3 Sorry to bother you, but your rubbish bin is in front of our house.
4 The problem's been going on for months!
5 I'm sorry about that. I'll make sure it's quiet tomorrow.

b **9.4**))) Listen again. Pause the listening and repeat after each sentence.

Writing taking part in online discussions

3a Read the online conversation. Match each blogger to an opinion.

1 Monica ___   2 Jurgen ___   3 Sandy ___

a We worry too much about other people's opinions of our clothes.
b Unconsciously, we tell the world about ourselves when we dress.
c Our clothes reveal what we wish to say about ourselves.

***Monica** Rome*
In *You Are What You Wear*, psychologist Dr Jennifer Baumgartner argues that our choice of clothing is a reflection of what we are thinking and feeling. What do you think? Do our clothes tell others who we really are?

***Jurgen** Salzburg*
[1] *That's a great question* . [2] _____.
Personally, I agree with Dr Baumgartner. Without even knowing it, we choose clothes that say everything about us – our age, our taste, our culture, our interests, and our lifestyle.

***Monica** Rome*
[3] _____ . [4] _____, our clothes must say something about ourselves. But I don't think it's subconscious – not always, anyway. I think we carefully select our clothes to present our best side to the world. We only show what we want people to see.

***Sandy** Cape Town*
[5] _____, Jurgen and Monica. In my opinion, we should be braver when choosing clothes, and shouldn't think about what others say. Often we choose clothes to look like everybody else. We should choose clothes that make us different.

---

b Read the online conversation again and complete it with the phrases and sentences in the box.

> As you say   Thanks for commenting on my post
> Thanks for posting it   ~~That's a great question~~
> You make some good points

I can ...	Very well	Quite well	More practice
use phrasal verbs.	○	○	○
make effective complaints.	○	○	○
take part in online discussions.	○	○	○

10 Compete and cooperate

10.1 Crowd-funding

business

1 Match the words in the box to sentences 1–7.

> a guarantee   a loan   a profit   a risk   an investor
> ~~cash~~   funding

1 You need money in notes and coins. _cash_
2 The bank will give you £5,000, but you have to pay it back in a year. _____
3 There is a danger that the business won't succeed and make money. _____
4 We need a promise that you will pay back the money we lend you whether or not the business is successful.

   _____
5 You also need a person or company to buy shares in your company in the hope that you will make money.

   _____
6 We will provide money for the specific purpose of buying new equipment. _____
7 I hope your business is a success and you make more money than you spend! _____

2 Complete the advice with the correct preposition.

1 Always invest _in_ companies that are secure.
2 Be aware that share prices can go down as well as increase _____ value.
3 Understand the market before setting _____ a new business.
4 If you decide to take _____ a loan, make sure that you can keep up with payments.
5 Avoid borrowing from any organization except your bank, even if you are short _____ cash at the weekend.

PRONUNCIATION linking

3 **10.1**)) Mark the linking sound in the phrases as in the example. Then listen and check. Listen again and repeat.

1 set‿up‿a business
2 give a guarantee
3 raise a million
4 meet an investor
5 short of cash

4 Choose the correct verbs to complete the text.

The dotcom kid

Entrepreneur Nick Bell, the dotcom kid, [1]*put / found / set* up his own online company in the 1990s when he was only fourteen. Like many young people, he started his online company without having to [2]*get / take / find* out a bank loan, or [3]*back / share / present* his ideas to investors. Nick was able to [4]*make / get / put* funding from advertisers who were keen to reach the teenagers who liked Nick's online magazine. His company quickly [5]*increased / became / raised* in value, and he started to [6]*do / take / make* a profit. By the time he was sixteen, Nick had earned almost a million pounds. He has never [7]*found / made / given* himself short of cash since! After selling his online magazine, he [8]*set / became / gave* an investor in other companies. He has [9]*raised / backed / increased* a variety of projects, sometimes [10]*sharing / setting / backing* the risk with other investors. Today, Nick Bell works for News International, one of the world's largest news corporations, and he continues to believe that you're never too young to get into business.

➔ **STUDY TIP** It is a good idea to learn phrasal verbs by categorizing them under a topic heading, for example *Money*: *set up, take out, pay back, pay off, get by, save up, splash out, rip off.*

Grammar passives

5 Choose the correct options to complete the sentences.

1 Tea *prepares / is prepared* by pouring hot water over tea leaves. The Chinese were the first to drink tea in the tenth century BC.

2 People probably *began / were begun* drinking coffee for the first time in Yemen during the fifteenth century.

3 Chocolate drinking vessels *have found / have been found* in Mayan tombs that are four thousand years old.

4 Beer dates back to 9,500 BC, when cereals *were farming / were being farmed* for the first time.

5 In the seventeenth century, market sellers *started / were started* selling lemonade on the streets of Paris.

6 Scotch whisky *made / was made* popular by King James IV, who really loved the drink.

6 Read the sentences from a story about toothpaste. Complete them with the verb in brackets in the correct passive form.

1 Toothpaste *was invented* by Washington Wentworth Sheffield. (invent)

2 It _____ for the first time in the 1880s. (sell)

3 Toothpaste _____ of a variety of ingredients including fluoride and sodium sulphate. (make)

4 Toothpaste in tubes _____ by the Colgate company since 1896. (manufacture)

5 Mint _____ to improve the taste of toothpaste. (use)

6 Nylon toothbrushes _____ by the DuPont chemical company in the 1930s. (introduce)

7 Complete the article with the correct active or passive form of the verbs in brackets.

Hungry for success

Businesswoman Shazia Saleem jokes that she **1** *started* (start) her food company, **ieat foods**, because she was hungry. It **2** _____ (set) up in 2013 to produce ready-made traditional British and Italian meals, such as shepherd's pie, which **3** _____ (make) of lamb and potatoes, and lasagne, which **4** _____ (contain) meat and pasta. Of course, these types of food **5** _____ (can/buy) in supermarkets and restaurants all over the world. What makes Shazia's meals different is the way they **6** _____ (prepare). Unlike most European dishes, Shazia's meals **7** _____ (make) using halal meat. Halal meat is meat that **8** _____ (prepare) according to Muslim dietary law. People whose cultural identity is both European and Muslim often **9** _____ (find) it difficult to buy ready-made halal food which isn't Asian. Now, thanks to Shazia, traditional European ready meals for Muslims **10** _____ (sell) in leading supermarkets for the first time.

I can …	Very well	Quite well	More practice
talk about business.	○	○	○
talk about how things are done.	○	○	○

10.2 Competitive sport

competitive sport

1 Unscramble the words in bold to complete the sentences.

1 Uruguay won the first football World Cup _final_ in 1930. **lanfi**

2 The great Brazilian Formula One World Champion Ayrton Senna was very _____ and always wanted to win. **mopectvetii**

3 Tiger Woods has won fourteen major golf _____ in his career so far. **otmatnesur**

4 Usain Bolt was a gold medal _____ in the 100 and 200 metres at the 2008 and 2012 Olympics. **rewnni**

5 In 2001, Samoa played _____ Australia in a football match, and lost 31–0. **stagnia**

6 The annual boat _____ between Oxford and Cambridge Universities took place for the first time in 1829. **ecar**

➡ **STUDY TIP** Scrambling words is a good way of revising them. Choose ten or twelve words you want to learn. Try to memorize them. Then write them at random on a piece of paper, scrambled. Return to the piece of paper later in the day and see how many words you can remember.

2 Complete the text with the correct form of the verbs in the box.

> break ~~compete~~ lose play take win

Sixteen teams [1] _competed_ in the 2011 FIFA Women's World Cup. In the final, Japan [2]_____ against the USA and [3]_____ the match in an exciting penalty shoot-out. They became the first Asian winners of the tournament.

Their win was surprising because, although the Japanese team had [4]_____ part in earlier tournaments, they hadn't been very successful. They had [5]_____ 8–0 to Sweden in 1991 and 5–0 to Russia in 1999. They had only won one match in the tournaments of 2003 and 2007. In the 2011 tournament, however, their top goalscorer Homare Sawa [6]_____ the record for scoring the most goals at a World Cup by an Asian player.

3 Complete the quick quiz with words and phrases from exercises **1** and **2**.

1 Which adjective describes a sportsperson who always wants to play and win?

competitive

2 Which word describes a competition when players or teams compete against each other in a number of matches, ending in a final?

_____

3 What do you call eleven players in football but five players in basketball?

_____

4 What do you call the Tour de France in cycling and the Monaco Grand Prix in motor sport?

_____

5 What do you call the last match in the football World Cup?

_____

Grammar using articles: *a/an, the,* – (no article)

4 Complete the famous sports quotes with *a, an, the* or – (no article).

❝ I've never lost ¹ _a_ game. I just ran out of ² _____ time. ❞
Michael Jordan
basketball superstar

❝ You are never ³ _____ loser until you stop trying. ❞
Mike Ditka
American football coach

❝ There are only three sports: ⁴ _____ bullfighting, ⁵ _____ motor racing, and ⁶ _____ mountaineering; all ⁷ _____ rest are merely ⁸ _____ games. ❞
Ernest Hemingway
novelist and sportsman

❝ I love ⁹ _____ Olympics, because they enable ¹⁰ _____ people from all over ¹¹ _____ world to come together and … accuse each other of ¹² _____ cheating. ❞
Dave Barry
American sports journalist

5a **10.2** 🔊 Listen to the phrases and notice the weak /ə/ sound in the pronunciation of *a, an* and *the*. Why is *the* pronounced differently in phrase 4?

1 lose a match
2 win an Olympic medal
3 break the record
4 take part in the Olympics

b **10.2** 🔊 Listen again and repeat the phrases.

6 Complete the text about how sport has changed the lives of two people. Use *a, an, the* or – (no article).

Sport changed my life

Judith Hamer

¹ _____ Life changed for Judith Hamer when, at ² _____ age of fifteen, she had her right leg amputated below ³ _____ knee. A year later, she was ⁴ _____ member of ⁵ _____ British wheelchair basketball team. She took part in ⁶ _____ London Olympics in 2012, and, although her team didn't win ⁷ _____ medal, they did really well, finishing seventh, which was better than they expected.

Joseph Kamau

Joseph Kamau is ⁸ _____ 33-year-old boxer from ⁹ _____ township of Kibera in South Africa. He had problems with ¹⁰ _____ drugs, and belonged to ¹¹ _____ violent street gang before he decided to join a boxing club organized by Fight for Peace, a charity that uses boxing and martial arts combined with education and personal development to realize ¹² _____ potential of young people in communities that suffer from violence and crime.

I can …	Very well	Quite well	More practice
talk about competition.	○	○	○
use definite, indefinite and zero articles.	○	○	○

10.3 Vocabulary development

Vocabulary phrases with *take* and *have*

1 Complete the sentences with *take* or *have* in the correct form.

1 Babe Ruth, the most famous baseball player in history, grew up in an orphanage because his parents couldn't _take_ care of him.

2 Although the Ryder Cup is one of the most famous trophies in sport, it _____ nothing to do with riding. It's a golf tournament between the USA and Europe.

3 Did you know that the second Football World Cup final _____ place in Italy in 1934?

4 England and Australia _____ turns to host a five-match cricket series every two years.

5 Did you know that legendary basketball player Michael Jordan _____ difficulties getting into his high school team?

6 Most countries didn't _____ beach volleyball seriously until it became an Olympic sport in the 1990s.

2a Choose the correct options to complete phrases 1–5.

1 *have / take* a feeling

2 *have / take* advantage of

3 *don't have / don't take* a clue

4 *have / take* your word for it

5 *have / take* a word with

b Jack (J) and Paul (P) are chatting at a football match. Match phrases 1–5 in exercise 2a to the phrases in italics with a similar meaning in the conversation.

J I ᵃ*don't know* who scored. _3_

P I ᵇ*think* it was Oscar. ___

J OK. I'll ᶜ*believe that*. ___

P I can ᵈ*speak to* the man behind us and find out for sure. ___

J Don't worry. I'll ᵉ*use* the half-time break to find out. ___

P Good idea.

Vocabulary review

3 Choose the correct words to complete the business phrases.

		a		b	
1	raise	a	(money)	b	an investor
2	share	a	the risk	b	short of cash
3	set up	a	profit	b	a business
4	present	a	an idea	b	in value
5	back	a	money	b	a project
6	become	a	an investor	b	funding
7	find yourself	a	in value	b	short of cash
8	get	a	the risk	b	funding
9	take out	a	a bank loan	b	a business
10	increase	a	an investor	b	in value
11	give	a	a project	b	a guarantee
12	make	a	a profit	b	the risk

4 Match the two halves of the sentences.

1 Polly lost _d_

2 Ahmed's team played ___

3 Edin took ___

4 Sylvia broke the ___

5 Aris was the winner ___

6 Jill competed for ___

a part in the tournament.

b European record.

c her school.

d the race.

e against Luis' team and they drew the match 1–1.

f of the final.

10.4 Speaking and writing

making recommendations

1 **10.3**))) Omar and Louisa have just arrived at the International Festival of Sports. Read the poster, then listen and tick the events they decide to go to.

INTERNATIONAL FESTIVAL OF SPORTS

This year, the international youth tournament takes place in Vienna, Austria from 3–6 July. Eleven- to twenty-one-year-olds will compete in a wide range of sports, including:

American football ✓   table tennis ____
basketball ____   tae kwon do ____
bowling ____   tennis ____
soccer ____   volleyball ____
swimming ____   wrestling ____

Come and join us!

2a **10.4**))) Match the two halves of the sentences. Then listen and check your answers.

1 I'd definitely recommend watching _e_
2 Don't miss the ____
3 It might be a good idea to buy ____
4 Thank you, that's a ____
5 That sounds ____
6 That's a good idea, but ____

a great suggestion.
b we have to leave then.
c basketball tournament.
d great!
e the March of Nations.
f a ticket in advance for that.

b **10.4**))) Listen again. Pause the listening after each sentence and repeat.

Writing **changes and differences**

3a Read the article describing changes in Dubai. Are sentences 1 and 2 true (T) or false (F)?

1 In contrast to the past, the city's buildings are much taller nowadays.   T / F
2 Dubai is larger than it was, and has lost all its traditional buildings.   T / F

No city in the world has changed as much as Dubai in the past sixty years. In fact, **¹** _compared_ to Dubai, cities like London and Paris have been living life in the slow lane! Thanks to the discovery of oil in the 1960s, the city has been transformed from a small fishing port to one of the world's most exciting and luxurious cities. **²**_____ in the past it was a city of sand-coloured, single-storey houses, **³**_____ a city of high-rise buildings, including the world's tallest hotels, and the world's highest tower, the Burj Khalifa. One of the most significant **⁴**_____ in the layout of the city has been the construction of man-made islands and luxurious hotels. In **⁵**_____ to other cities in the region, Dubai has developed as a major tourist attraction and is one of the best places to go shopping in the world. **⁶**_____ people used to do all their shopping in markets, **⁷**_____ they drive to one of the many luxury shopping malls in the city. However, despite all the construction, it still retains its traditional heart – the markets and mosques along the banks of the Dubai Creek.

b Complete the article with the words in the box.

changes ~~compared~~ contrast now now it is whereas
whilst before

I can …	Very well	Quite well	More practice
understand phrases and expressions with *take* and *have*.	○	○	○
ask for, make and respond to recommendations.	○	○	○

10.5 Reading for pleasure

Nelson Mandela

1 Match the two halves of the sentences to find out about the early life of Nelson Mandela.

1 He was born on ___f___

2 His first name was Rolihlahla, ___

3 He was the first member ___

4 His father died when he ___

5 He joined the ANC* in ___

6 He was sentenced ___

a was nine, and he was brought up by his uncle, the king of the Thembu people.

b of his family to attend school.

c 1944 to fight apartheid**.

d to life in prison in 1964 for political crimes.

e but he was called Nelson when he went to school.

f July 18, 1918, in a very small village in South Africa.

2 Read this extract about the day he left prison, from *Nelson Mandela* by Rowena Akinyemi.

3 Why do you think Mandela was such a great leader and statesman?

On 11 February 1990, as the world watched on their televisions, Mandela walked with dignity towards the gate of Victor Verster Prison. He was tall, handsome, and looked younger than his seventy-one years. He smiled at the waiting crowd as he walked to freedom. 'As I finally walked through those gates to enter a car on the other side,' he wrote later, 'I felt – even at the age of seventy-one – that my life was beginning anew'. His prison days were over.

Mandela was driven, with Winnie[1], to City Hall in Cape Town. The crowd was so great that at first they could not get out of the car. As he stood in front of the crowd, he lifted his hand and said: 'Amandla! Amandla![2]' He told the crowd that apartheid had no future in South Africa, and that talks between the government and the ANC were beginning: 'I therefore place the remaining years of my life in your hands,' he told the people.

Mandela spent his first night of freedom at Archbishop Tutu's home in Cape Town, and then the next day he flew to Johannesburg. Thousands of people surrounded his old home in Orlando West, so they flew by helicopter to Soweto Stadium. There, 120,000 people were waiting to welcome Mandela back to Soweto. He told the crowd that his return to Soweto filled his heart with happiness, but he also felt a deep sadness, because their suffering under apartheid was not over. But apartheid would end soon, and the violence in the townships must also end.

That night, Mandela returned to Number 8115 Orlando West. People sang and danced outside the house, full of happiness that he was home again. The four-roomed house had been rebuilt after the fire[3], and at last Mandela knew that his prison days were over.

Text extract from *Oxford Bookworms Library: Nelson Mandela*

---

* **ANC** (African National Congress) – a movement founded in 1912 by four young African lawyers. They wanted to change South Africa so that Africans could be elected to parliament and could own land; they believed that Africans should work together to get better conditions for black people in South Africa

** **apartheid** – the former official government policy in South Africa of separating people of different races and making them live apart

[1] **Winnie was Mandela's second wife. They were married from 1958 to 1996.**

[2] *Amandla* **means 'power'.**

[3] **Winnie and Mandela's house had been set on fire by criminals two years earlier.**

Review: Units 9 and 10

Grammar

1 Choose the correct options to complete the sentences.

1 In the painting, the people in the background (could)/ *must / can't* be walking home from work, or just going for a walk. I'm not really sure.

2 Have you got *– / a / the* paintbrush you can lend me?

3 They are holding an outdoor exhibition in *– / an / the* park on Sunday.

4 In my opinion, a photograph is *much / less / even* powerful than a portrait painting.

5 Peter *must / might / can't* be in his studio. I'm sure of it. We've looked in every other room.

2 Complete the sentences with comparatives or superlatives. Use exactly **three** words including the words in brackets. Change the form of the adjective if necessary.

1 Starting a company is _much more difficult_ these days. (much/difficult)

2 Competitive sports aren't _____ they once were in my school. (as/popular)

3 Being an employee is _____ working on your own. (far/easy)

4 He is probably _____ artist in the country. (talented)

3 Complete the text with the correct form of the words in brackets.

The legend of William Webb Ellis

According to legend, the game of rugby **1** _was invented_ (invent) at Rugby School in England in the 1820s when the ball **2** _____ (pick) up by a schoolboy called William Webb Ellis during a game of football. He ran the length of the field, carrying the ball with his hands. Ever since then, two games **3** _____ (play) in Britain and across the world – football and rugby.

The Webb Ellis story is almost certainly not true. Today, the modern game of rugby **4** _____ (name) 'rugby' after Webb Ellis' school, but it is very different from any sport that he ever played. The first rules of the game **5** _____ (not write) until 1845, and the Rugby Football Union (or RFU) **6** _____ (not form) until the 1870s. Since 1987, when the first Rugby World Cup **7** _____ (hold) in New Zealand, the winners **8** _____ (give) a trophy called the Webb Ellis Cup, named in honour of a man who probably didn't invent the game of rugby.

Vocabulary

4 Write the words in the correct space in each sentence. There is one word you do not need.

1 | aged   shape   made   built |

Tom is a middle-_aged_ man in his fifties, well-_____ and in good _____ for his age.

2 | fringe   stubble   spiky   large |

The man I saw had _____ hair and a _____ jaw, with _____ on his chin.

3 | final   team   race   tournament |

Our young _____ played well in the _____ but didn't reach the _____.

4 | stories   bright   detailed   straight |

Poussin's paintings are often very _____, showing many figures and lots of action. He used _____ colours and told classical _____ in his works.

5 | bottom   middle   seems   mysterious |

In the _____ left-hand corner, you can see a _____ figure dressed in black, who _____ to be pointing into the distance.

Speaking

5 Match the two halves of the sentences.

1 Can I help you _c_

2 I wonder if you ___

3 I'd definitely recommend ___

4 I suggest that ___

5 OK, thanks. I'll ___

a you try a smaller pair.

b these shoes. They're much better quality.

c with anything else?

d could help me?

e give it a go.

11.1 Outlaws

1 Circle the word that doesn't belong in each category.

1 TYPES OF CRIME
   a burglary   b (prison)   c robbery

2 TYPES OF CRIMINAL
   a thief   b outlaw   c victim

3 WHAT THE POLICE DO
   a arrest   b escape   c capture

4 WHAT CRIMINALS DO
   a suspect   b steal   c rob

➡ **STUDY TIP** Use categorization to record and remember new words. Organize words into groups depending on topic, function or part of speech.

2 Complete the newspaper headlines with the correct form of the words provided.

1
> **Criminal gang sentenced to ten years for** _burglary_

BURGLE

2
> **Millions of dollars in _____ goods taken from millionaire's home**

STEAL

3
> **Thief _____ by police after four-hour car chase**

CAPTURE

4
> **Two dangerous bank _____ arrested**

ROB

5
> **Princess reports _____ of valuable golden necklace**

THIEF

6
> **Teenager arrested for _____ teacher's rare books**

STEAL

3a How are these *-ed* endings pronounced: /t/, /d/ or /ɪd/?

1 sentenced _/t/_   3 suspected ___   5 arrested ___
2 robbed ___   4 escaped ___

b **11.1**))) Listen, check and repeat.

4 Complete the crime stories with words from the box. There are three words you do not need.

> arrested burglar burglary escaped rob sentenced
> ~~steal~~ stolen suspected theft

In Kentucky, USA ...

In March 2014, James Stewart had to go to court and was worried about being late. So he decided to ¹ _steal_ a car and drive there! When he arrived, he was ² _____ by the police outside the courthouse, and later ³ _____ to six months in prison for car ⁴ _____.

In Berlin, Germany ...

In April 2013, a thirty-year-old man called the emergency services after he fell off the roof of a historic city centre building and broke his leg. The police arrived to help but quickly began to ask questions. The man was ⁵ _____ of being a ⁶ _____ because he was carrying a bag of ⁷ _____ goods from the building.

Grammar   unreal past conditional

5 Outlaws Bonnie Parker and Clyde Barrow are famous for living a life of crime in 1930s America. But their lives could have been very different. Complete the sentences with the phrases in the box. Use each phrase once.

had made   ~~hadn't been~~   hadn't left   hadn't shot
hadn't spent   have become   might never   not have died
would probably have   wouldn't have

1 If Bonnie and Clyde _hadn't been_ so poor, they probably _____ become bank robbers.
2 If Clyde _____ time in prison when he was a teenager, he _____ got a job and become an ordinary citizen.
3 Bonnie _____ have met Clyde Barrow if her first husband _____ her in 1929.
4 If they _____ and killed a policeman in 1932, they wouldn't _____ America's most wanted outlaws.
5 On 23 May 1934, six policemen shot Bonnie and Clyde in their car. They might _____ if they _____ different choices in their lives.

PRONUNCIATION   linking and intonation

6a **11.2**)) If a sentence is long and hard to say, practise using backchaining (i.e. say the last part of the sentence first). Listen and repeat the different parts of the long sentence below until you can say the whole sentence.

… probably have escaped.
… they'd probably have escaped.
… hadn't shot anyone, they'd probably have escaped.
If they hadn't shot anyone, they'd probably have escaped.

b **11.3**)) Practise saying the two sentences below using backchaining. Then listen and check.

1 They might have // lived longer // if they'd // stopped committing crimes.
2 Bonnie probably // wouldn't have been shot // if she hadn't // stayed with Clyde.

7 Complete the text with the words in brackets in the correct form.

Public Enemy Number 1

GET·DILLINGER!
$15,000 *Reward*
A PROCLAMATION

The early 1930s were called the 'public enemy era' in the United States because there were so many robbers, murderers and outlaws on the roads. There [1] _probably wouldn't have been_ (probably/not be) so many outlaws if the times [2] _____ (not be) so hard, but this was the period of the Great Depression when millions of Americans were poor and unemployed. If twenty-one-year-old John Dillinger [3] _____ (find) a job, he [4] _____ (probably/not commit) his first crime, the theft of $50 from a grocery store. Dillinger was sentenced to ten years in prison. If his father [5] _____ (not tell) young John to admit to the crime, he [6] _____ (probably/not go) to prison at all. By the time Dillinger came out of prison in 1933, he had decided to follow a life of crime. He formed the Dillinger Gang with people he had met in prison. If he [7] _____ (not spend) so long in prison, he [8] _____ (probably/not know) so many other criminals! They carried out lots of violent bank robberies and killed a policeman in Florida. John Dillinger was Public Enemy Number 1. Unfortunately for Dillinger, however, that made him a target for a new organization called the FBI, the Federal Bureau of Investigation. If FBI agents [9] _____ (not start) following his gang, John Dillinger [10] _____ (might/escape). However, he was recognized by FBI agents as he left a theatre in Chicago, and they shot and killed him.

I can …	Very well	Quite well	More practice
talk about crime.	○	○	○
talk about an unreal past.	○	○	○

11.2 *I should never have clicked 'send'!*

behaviour on social media

1 Choose the correct verbs to complete the blog entries.

> ☒
>
> # Tony's blog
>
> Everybody **1** (*regrets*)/ *upsets* sending at least one email. Have you ever thought, 'Oh, why did I send that?!' Write and tell me your experience.
>
> *Patricia*
> Once, I accidentally **2** *insulted* / *regretted* my boss when I wrote an email to him. His name's *Jose*, and I wrote *Dear Joke* by mistake.
>
> *Lance*
> I don't usually **3** *feel* / *show* passionate enough to send angry emails, but once, about ten years ago, I wrote a rude email to an annoying colleague. I really wish I hadn't. Now, he's the managing director.
>
> *Sylvie*
> Once, I sent a list of complaints to my manager. She didn't speak to me for weeks. I know now you should never write what you wouldn't **4** *say* / *tell* to someone's face.
>
> *Artur*
> I didn't get any emails yesterday, and it was my birthday. That really **5** *upset* / *criticized* me.

2 Unscramble the adjectives in brackets to complete the story.

The email I wish I'd never sent

After my girlfriend left me, I was so angry that I wrote an email that was really **1** _rude_ (edur). I insulted her in every way I could think of. I criticized her intelligence, and I criticized her appearance, which was really, really **2**_____ (satyn). I am naturally a very **3**_____ (openatsisa) person, who gets angry easily. And I suppose I can say **4**_____ (lapsetnnua) things when I'm upset or angry. But that's no excuse. Now, of course, I deeply **5**_____ (geerte) what I did, because she was so **6**_____ (tuspe) that she has never replied to any of my emails, texts or **7**_____ (ewetst) since. If I had just thought about it, I would never have sent that email, and that would have made a real **8**_____ (efredicfne) to my life because, although Sally didn't want to be my girlfriend, there was no reason why we couldn't have been friends.

word stress

3a **11.4** 》 Listen and circle the word in each list with stress on the second syllable.

1 nasty	(insult)	victim
2 criticize	passionate	unpleasant
3 regret	bully	careless
4 blogging	issue	upset

b **11.4** 》 Listen again and repeat.

4 Complete the online article with the correct form of the words in the box.

> careless   feel   ~~make~~   nasty   replaced   say   speak
> stand   victim   upset

Keep your secrets offline

Social networking has **1** _made_ a real difference to how and when we talk about ourselves. To some extent, it has **2**_____ face-to-face interaction. Nowadays, it seems, we are free to express views about people that we would never **3**_____ to their face, and we are free to talk about ourselves in ways that, in the past, we would never have done. We are free to **4**_____ up about issues we **5**_____ passionate about, which is a good thing, but we are also free to talk about our personal secrets, or those of our friends. Now that social networking is so commonplace, we forget that we're not just talking to friends when we use it. We are often **6**_____ about what we say, and this can get us into trouble.

Here are a few reminders of what you might <u>not</u> want to do on the most popular social networking sites:

1 Never say that you hate your job. This will **7**_____ your boss if he or she reads it, and that'll be the end of the job!

2 It's OK to **8**_____ up for what you believe in, but don't get into an argument and start saying really horrible, **9**_____ things about people. Don't get personal.

3 Don't say how good you are, or constantly ask friends and colleagues for *likes* and *comments*. It's boring.

4 And don't post pictures of friends without their permission. If other people start commenting on their appearance they may become a **10**_____ of cyberbullying.

Grammar *should/shouldn't have*

5a Put the words in order to make sentences that express criticisms.

1 spoken / should / she / have / up .
   She should have spoken up.

2 shouldn't / other / celebrities / criticized / they / have .
   They _____

3 he / been / have / so / should / critical ?
   Should _____

4 tweet / he / sent / have / that / shouldn't / nasty .
   He _____

5 you / been / should / more / have / careful .
   You _____

6 you / studying / shouldn't / be / your / for / exams ?
   Shouldn't _____

b **11.5**))) Listen to the sentences from exercise **5a** and check your answers. Notice the word linking and the weak pronunciation of *have*.

c **11.5**))) Listen again and repeat the sentences.

6 Read the situations. Then write criticisms using *should* or *shouldn't*.

1 Aris posted a video on the Web without his friend's permission.
   He _____ the video!

2 Penny sent a critical text message to her boss.
   She _____ the text!

3 Anja didn't speak to her parents about the rude email she'd received.
   She _____ to her parents!

4 Laurence didn't join Twitter until last month.
   He _____ Twitter sooner.

5 Kerry hasn't written in her blog yet.
   She _____ in her blog already.

6 Alain spent eight hours on the internet last night.
   He _____ so long on the internet.

7 Samir didn't reply to any of my emails.
   He _____ to my emails.

8 Annie posted a photo of Sarah without her permission.
   Annie _____ the photo of Sarah.

7 Complete the text with *should* or *shouldn't* and the correct form of the verbs in brackets.

Should the famous tweet?

'I don't understand why any famous person would ever be on Twitter.' George Clooney

Should Hollywood star George Clooney **1** *have expressed* (express) that view back in 2013? There are, no doubt, some Twitter executives who strongly believe he **2** _____ (not say) it, but I'm sure most of us would agree that there are plenty of public figures who really **3** _____ (listen) to him. One famous actor, for example, used rude, nasty language to criticize a journalist he hated on Twitter. He really **4** _____ (not threaten) the journalist in that way. It went viral and hurt his career. And a well-known American politician got into trouble for losing his temper on Twitter. He **5** _____ (think) twice before sending unpleasant tweets. Footballers have got into trouble, too. One England international footballer was sold by his club after he used Twitter to criticize them. He **6** _____ (not do) that. And another player **7** _____ (not post) a funny picture of a referee he disliked on Twitter, either. He was fined £10,000 by the English Football Association.

The problem for celebrities is that they are also criticized for not being on Twitter. Actor Hugh Laurie, the star of the American TV series *House*, **8** _____ (realize) that he would regret saying he'd never use Twitter. Two years later, he felt he had to join because his fans wanted to hear from him. **9** _____ (he/join) the endless chatter on Twitter? Only time will tell.

I can …	Very well	Quite well	More practice
criticize past actions.	○	○	○
talk about people's behaviour on social networking sites.	○	○	○

11.3 Vocabulary development

words with multiple meanings

1   Complete the sentences with five words from the box in the correct form. Use each word twice.

> bank change fine jam key light match rock
> shower square wave

1   As we sailed away on the great ship, we __waved__ goodbye to the crowds on the shore. All that lay between us and America were the strong winds and the high, powerful _____ of the Atlantic Ocean.

2   It was a _____, sunny day, so we stopped the car by the beach and went for a swim. When we got back, there was a parking ticket on my windscreen. I had to pay a £100 _____!

3   I climbed into the attic and lit a _____ to see where I was going. I found dozens of old programmes from football _____ that my great-grandfather had been to in 1937.

4   Although we'd _____ some money at the airport, when we arrived we realized we didn't have any coins for the trolley. We had to buy a newspaper so we could get some _____.

5   I was caught in several heavy _____ on my way home. I was so wet and dirty by the time I got in that Mum told me to go upstairs and have a _____ straightaway!

2   Complete the pairs of phrases with words from the box in exercise **1**. Use the same word in each pair.

1   a   a traffic _jam_   b   tea, toast and _jam_
2   a   a city _____   b   a _____ shape
3   a   a sun _____   b   an electric _____
4   a   a heavy _____ music   b   an enormous _____
5   a   a river _____ b   savings _____
6   a   a answer _____ b   door _____

Vocabulary review

3   Match the two halves of the sentences.
1   Firth was sentenced _d_
2   James is suspected ___
3   Thomas was arrested ___
4   Richards has escaped ___
5   Andrews has stolen ___
6   The police hope to catch ___

a   of more than twenty robberies.
b   over a thousand dollars in cash.
c   the violent robber.
d   to life in prison.
e   by a policeman who chased and caught him.
f   from prison again.

4   Add the words in the box to the correct categories.

> burglar ~~robbery~~ steal theft

1   CRIMES
    1 _robbery_   burglary   2 _____

2   CRIMINALS
    robber   thief   3 _____

3   VERBS
    rob   4 _____

5   Complete the advice with words from the box.

> criticize cyber face feel issues make ~~regret~~
> replace rude speak stand upset

1   Don't send texts you will later _regret_ sending. Think first.
2   Don't _____ the appearance of other people. Be polite. Don't be _____ and nasty. If you are unpleasant, you will _____ people!
3   _____ up about things you _____ passionate about.
4   Blogging and tweeting about _____ that are important to you can _____ a difference.
5   If you are a victim of _____ bullying, tell someone.
6   Always _____ up for what you believe in.
7   Never write things about a person on social networking sites that you wouldn't say to his or her _____.
8   Blogging and tweeting have started to _____ face-to-face interaction, so think about what you want to say when you click 'send'.

11.4 Speaking and writing

decisions

1a **11.6** ⟩ Listen to two conversations. Decide whether the statements are true about Conversation 1, 2 or both.

1 The conversation takes place in a college or university.
   Conversation 1   Conversation 2   ⟨both⟩

2 It's break time.
   Conversation 1   Conversation 2   both

3 The speakers are all students.
   Conversation 1   Conversation 2   both

4 They are worried about people arriving late.
   Conversation 1   Conversation 2   both

5 They think that lectures start too early.
   Conversation 1   Conversation 2   both

6 They make a decision to say or ask something.
   Conversation 1   Conversation 2   both

b **11.6** ⟩ Complete the phrases with a verb from the box in the correct form. Listen again and check your answers.

> admit   be   convince   ~~move~~   run   settle

1 Could we _move_ on?
2 I'm _____ that we need to be a lot stricter.
3 You must _____ that the problem would soon be solved if ...
4 That's _____, then.
5 We're _____ out of time.
6 _____ there any other suggestions?

c Match phrases 1–6 in exercise **1b** to categories a–d.
   a Controlling the time   _1_, ___
   b Making your point stronger   ___, ___
   c Discussing options   ___
   d Arriving at a decision   ___

2a Read Conversation 3. Complete it with phrases from exercise **1**.

Conversation 3

Chairperson   OK. That's decided. Could [1] _we move on_ ? The next item on the agenda is lunch times. Should they be longer?

Student representative   In our opinion, they should be longer. You [2]_____ students work harder when they've had a good long break and plenty to eat.

Staff representative   I'm not so sure. A longer lunchtime means a late finish to the day, and students get tired late in the day.

Chairperson   OK. Well, a late finish is just one possibility. Another [3]_____ an earlier start.

Student representative   That's a good idea. An earlier start and a longer lunchtime.

Staff representative   I agree.

Chairperson   OK. That's [4]_____. We'll start lectures at the college thirty minutes earlier.

b **11.7** ⟩ Listen and check your answers. Do you think the other students in Conversation 2 will like this idea? Why/Why not?

apologizing

3 Complete the sentences with the words in the box. Use each word once only.

> apologies   apologize   forgive   hope   inconvenience
> ~~sorry~~   understand

1 I'm so _sorry_ for missing your birthday party.
2 We _____ you understand that the reasons for the delay were out of our hands.
3 Please _____ me.
4 Please accept our _____ for the late delivery and for the _____ this causes.
5 I can _____ that it would have been better to post it earlier.
6 I _____ for the trouble this has caused.

I can ...	Very well	Quite well	More practice
understand words with multiple meanings.	○	○	○
come to a decision.	○	○	○
apologize in writing.	○	○	○

Influence

12.1 Advertising

advertising

1   Complete the text with words from the box.

> adverts   billboards   brands   logos   posters   ~~products~~
> slogans

The cost of advertising

Major advertising companies are prepared to spend millions to launch new ¹ _products_ . They spend money on placing ² _____ in magazines and online, and on putting up huge ³_____ on giant ⁴_____ which can be seen by commuters as they travel or drive into our city centres. High-paid advertising executives think up ⁵_____, such as *A Mars a day helps you work, rest and play*; and create ⁶_____, such as the McDonald's 'M' or the Nike swoosh. The costs are amazing. Car manufacturer *Acura* spent $78 million in 2013 on an advertising campaign as they tried to compete with other very well-known ⁷_____ of luxury cars. And *Chrysler* spent $9 million on one TV advertisement, which starred the rapper Eminem!

word stress

2a **12.1** 🔊 Listen and circle the word in each list with the stress on the second syllable.

1 billboard	(amusing)	slogan
2 memorable	advert	persuasive
3 product	confusing	clever
4 effective	logo	poster

b   **12.1** 🔊 Listen again. Pause after each word and repeat.

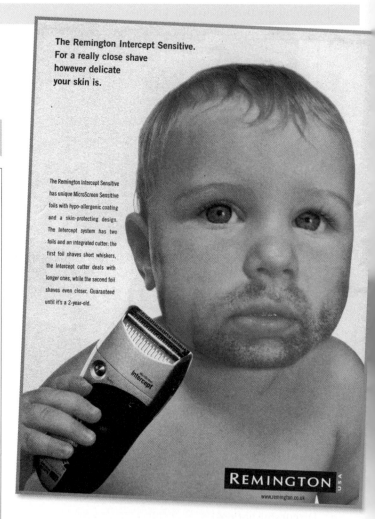

The Remington Intercept Sensitive. For a really close shave however delicate your skin is.

The Remington Intercept Sensitive has unique MicroScreen Sensitive foils with hypo-allergenic coating and a skin-protecting design. The Intercept system has two foils and an integrated cutter: the first foil shaves short whiskers, the Intercept cutter deals with longer ones, while the second foil shaves even closer. Guaranteed until it's a 2-year-old.

REMINGTON USA
www.remington.co.uk

3   Look at the advertisement above and match the people's responses 1–6 to words a–f.

1   I think it's funny. I laughed and laughed.   _d_

2   It isn't very nice, showing a baby with stubble – urgh! ____

3   I'll always remember seeing this for the first time. ____

4   What an intelligent, original way of selling something! ____

5   I'm going to buy this for my husband. ____

6   I don't really understand what it's trying to sell. ____

a clever		d amusing
b memorable		e unpleasant
c confusing		f persuasive

4 Complete the text with the missing words.

The greatest ad in history

In 1959, New York advertising agency DDB launched a campaign to sell a fairly new **1**p*roduct* in America – the Volkswagen Beetle. Although Volkswagen was a popular **2**b_____ in Europe because of its famous VW **3**l_____ and its attractive design, Americans showed little interest in it. They loved big cars, and in the 1950s, so soon after World War II, they didn't like anything German. DDB designed newspaper and magazine **4**a_____ that were so **5**m_____ that people can still recall them today. They came up with the **6**s_____ 'Think Small' which was really **7**c_____ because, in two words, they managed to tell Americans to think about the Beetle and to change their way of seeing the world. Other ads they used were really **8**a_____ . In one, for example, they showed a New York policeman sitting in a VW beetle with the words 'Don't laugh' under the picture. The campaign was **9**p_____ – many Americans changed the way they viewed cars. And it was **10**e_____ – sales of VWs increased rapidly, and the car remains popular in the US today. *AdAge* magazine voted DDB's campaign the greatest in history.

Think small.

Grammar reported speech

5 Read the reported feedback on a new advertisement. Choose the correct option to complete the direct speech.

1 The sales manager said it was a brilliant advertisement.
   'It *is* / *was* a brilliant advertisement.'

2 The head designer told us that they hadn't designed the poster yet.
   'We *don't design* / *haven't designed* the poster yet.'

3 The finance manager said he was trying to find out how much it would cost to produce.
   'I *am* / *was* trying to find out how much it *will* / *has* cost to produce.'

4 The client said that it wouldn't sell their product.
   'It *doesn't* / *won't* sell our product.'

6 Report the famous quotes about advertising.

1 'Advertising is the greatest art form of the 20th century.'
   Canadian philosopher Marshall McLuhan once said that _advertising was the greatest art form of the 20th century_ .

2 'Many a small thing has been made large by the right kind of advertising.'
   Nineteenth-century American author Mark Twain said that _____ by the right kind of advertising.

3 'Ninety-nine per cent of advertising doesn't sell anything.'
   British advertising executive David Ogilvy said that _____.

4 'Advertising has done more to cause the social unrest of the 20th century than any other single factor.'
   American author and politician Clare Booth Luce thought that _____ the social unrest of the 20th century than any other single factor.

5 'You never see good poetry in advertising.'
   English poet David Whyte told an interviewer that _____.

6 'I left advertising as fast as I could.'
   American novelist Elmore Leonard said that he _____.

7 Read comments from an interview with a young advertising copywriter. Then complete the reported sentences.

'(1) I'm a junior copywriter. I'm learning how to design ads and write slogans. (2) I started working here at WPP in London last year. (3) It is one of the largest advertising agencies in the country. (4) My job involves designing adverts for our clients' products. (5) I am really busy now. (6) I'm hoping to be promoted next month.'

1 He said that _he was a junior copywriter and was learning how to design ads and write slogans_ .

2 He told us that _____ the previous year.

3 He said that WPP _____ in the country.

4 He told us that his job_____ products.

5 He said that _____ then.

6 He said that _____ the following month.

→ STUDY TIP Remember: *You say something* but *You tell someone something*.

I can …	Very well	Quite well	More practice
talk about advertising.	○	○	○
understand and use reported speech.	○	○	○

12.2 How to persuade and influence people

Vocabulary persuading people

1 Phrases 1–6 all mean that you persuaded everybody to see your point of view. Complete them with the verbs in the box in the past simple form.

> bring   convince   get   overcome   ~~see~~   win

1 In the end, everybody _saw_ things my way.
2 I _____ people round to my way of thinking.
3 I _____ people over.
4 I _____ my own way.
5 I _____ everybody I was right.
6 Eventually, I _____ everybody's objections to my ideas.

PRONUNCIATION linking

2a **12.2**))) Listen and mark the linking between the ends and beginnings of words.
1 I won them over.
2 He got his own way.
3 They brought us round to their way of thinking.
4 She saw it my way.

b **12.2**))) Listen again and repeat.

3 Complete the text by adding three words from the box to each space. Use each word once.

> bring   convince   ~~friends~~   ~~our~~   our   over   own
> ~~persuade~~   round   them   to   us   us   way   win

Grammar reported questions

4 Choose the sentence (a or b) that is being reported in the extracts from a marketing survey.

1 The market researcher asked if I would answer some questions.
   a Did you answer any questions?
   b Will you answer some questions?
2 She said that it wouldn't take very long.
   a It won't take very long.
   b It doesn't take very long.
3 She asked me what type of breakfast cereal I ate.
   a What type of breakfast cereal do you eat?
   b What type of breakfast cereal have you eaten?
4 She asked if I had thought about changing my cereal.
   a Do you think about changing your cereal?
   b Have you thought about changing your cereal?
5 She asked if I wanted to try new Top Pops.
   a Do you want to try new Top Pops?
   b Did you want to try new Top Pops?

The five most persuasive words in English

There are times when we've all wished we had the words to ¹ _persuade our friends_ to do things, or
² _____ to our way of thinking. How wonderful it would be if we had the words to get
³ _____ all the time – to always be able to do what we want. Well, in the world of advertising, copywriters do have the words. In fact, they have five magic words that they regularly use to ⁴ _____ .
We simply can't say 'no' when they use them! The first

of these words is 'you'. When 'you' is used in an advert, we think that the ad is speaking to us directly, and we are more likely to be open to its message. Advertisers also
⁵ _____ buy things by using words like 'free', 'new' and 'instantly', all of which are very appealing. One last word advertisers use is 'because'. When advertisers use 'because', they give a reason for buying their product. *Because it's fresher!* they say, or *Because it's newer*. And, believe it or not, most of us tend to accept that reason.

5 Order the words to form reported questions from an interview with an advertising executive.

1 worked / long / the interviewer / me / had / in advertising / how / asked / I .
The interviewer *asked me how long I had worked in advertising.*

2 why / that job / I / apply / he / had / wondered / to / decided / for .
He _____

3 asked / at / I / was / what / he / projects / that time / on / working .
He _____

4 to / hoping / he / few months / I / next / asked / be promoted / me / was / the / in / if .
He _____

5 what / asked / I / about / he / job / found / me / my / interesting .
He _____

6 Brussels / back / the next day / he / if / to / going / travel / to / asked / was / me / I .
He _____

6 Write the direct questions.
1 *How long have you worked in advertising?*
2 _____
3 _____
4 _____
5 _____
6 _____

7 Here are some other questions from the interview. Write reported questions.
1 Can you tell me about an advertising campaign that hasn't worked?
The interviewer asked me _____
2 Why do you think it failed?
The interviewer asked me _____
3 Have you ever been in a situation where you have led a team?
He _____
4 How did others respond to your leadership?
He _____
5 Do you ever have disagreements with your clients about marketing plans?
He _____
6 What do you do to resolve those disagreements?
He _____

8 The young woman who was interviewed got the job! Read what she told her friends about it and correct the errors.
1 The interviewer called and asked me when can I start.
The interviewer called and asked me when I could start.
2 He asked me will you sign the work contract this afternoon.
_____
3 He asked me what hours do you want to work.
_____
4 He asked that I am ready to start work here next Monday.
_____
5 He asked me how much did they pay me in your last job.
_____
6 He asked are you prepared to work in our office abroad.
_____

I can …	Very well	Quite well	More practice
talk about persuasion.	○	○	○
understand and use reported questions.	○	○	○

12.3 Vocabulary development

Vocabulary **dependent prepositions**

1 Choose the correct dependent prepositions to complete the sentences.

1 If we are interested *at / on / in* the culture of another country, we tend to like the people there.

2 People around the world love Brazilians because they are so good *at / in / on* football.

3 Everybody knows what a huge red M refers *about / to / for*. It's an iconic symbol of globalization – and burgers!

4 British pop music succeeded *in / to / about* developing a worldwide following in the 1960s.

5 When they want to buy clothes or shoes, many people look *on / for / about* Italian designer labels.

6 People who work *in / to / for* Nissan or Toyota in Europe have a very positive view of Japan.

2 Complete the text with the missing dependent prepositions.

Soft Power

For anybody who is interested ¹ *in* politics or worries ² _____ the world's future, Joseph S. Nye's best-seller *Soft Power: The Means to Success In World Politics* is a book they must read. Nye invented the phrase 'soft power' to describe how the attractiveness of a country's culture, ideals and policies could influence other countries, and naturally, he really believes ³ _____ the idea. In his book, Nye talks ⁴ _____ how powerful governments should concentrate ⁵ _____ spreading a positive message rather than using 'hard power' to make other countries afraid ⁶ _____ them. If people in a country are listening ⁷ _____ your pop music, eating your fast food and working ⁸ _____ your multinational companies, this will inevitably lead ⁹ _____ better relations with these countries. Although he accepts that countries like the US should sometimes use their 'hard power', their military or economic strength, he believes that a peaceful future for the world ultimately depends ¹⁰ _____ the use of soft power.

Vocabulary review

3 Unscramble the words to make advertising words.

1 vreadt   *advert*
2 oglo   _____
3 abbolidrl   _____
4 danbr   _____
5 restop   _____
6 crudtpo   _____
7 angols   _____

4 Match adjectives 1–7 to sentences a–g that have a similar meaning.

1 persuasive   a It's funny.
2 clever   b I don't understand it.
3 effective   c It isn't nice.
4 amusing   d It's intelligent.
5 memorable   e It makes me want to buy it.
6 unpleasant   f It works really well.
7 confusing   g I won't forget it.

5 Complete the phrases with one word.

1 convince someone you're *right*
2 get your _____ way
3 bring people _____ to your way of thinking
4 see things their _____
5 win people _____

12.4 Speaking and writing

Speaking agreeing and disagreeing

1a **12.3**))) Listen to three short conversations at an advertising agency. Choose the correct options to complete the sentences.

Conversation 1

1 The two speakers are talking about an advert for …
   a a skirt.   b a pair of trousers.
2 In the end, the two speakers …
   a agree.   b disagree.

Conversation 2

1 The two speakers are talking about an advert for …
   a a watch.   b a necklace.
2 In the end, the two speakers …
   a agree.   b disagree.

Conversation 3

1 The three speakers are talking about an advert for …
   a a new lipstick.   b a new toothpaste.
2 In the end, the three speakers …
   a agree.   b disagree.

b **12.3**))) Listen again and tick the two phrases that the speakers use in each conversation.

Conversation 1

Asking if someone agrees

a Would you agree? ___
b Don't you agree? ___
c What's your view? ___
d Wouldn't you say …? ___

Conversation 2

Disagreeing

a I'm not sure about that. ___
b Yes, but I can't help thinking … ___
c Well, I agree up to a point, but … ___
d I totally disagree. ___

Conversation 3

Agreeing

a I couldn't agree more. ___
b That's a good point. ___
c That's just what I was thinking. ___
d You might be right. ___

Writing advantages and disadvantages essay

2a Read the essay and choose the best title.

1 What are the advantages of selling our clothes online?
2 Should we shop for clothes online or not?
3 Are clothes online better than those in the high street?

These days, more and more people are buying their clothes on the internet rather than in the high street. Obviously, this is bad news for high-street shops. But is it also something that we, as consumers, should think more carefully about before we click on the basket icon and make our purchases? Are there **[1]disadvantages as well as advantages to** buying clothes online?

There are, of course, **[2]a number of advantages** to shopping online. **[3]A significant advantage** is that it is quick and easy. **[4]A further advantage** is that it tends to be much cheaper because we can shop around to find a bargain. Online retail sites also have fewer costs than high-street shops. so they can keep their prices low.

On the other hand, there are **[5]a number of disadvantages to** buying everything online. **[6]A significant disadvantage** is that you can't try on clothes when you shop online, so you might choose the wrong size or colour, or find out that an item of clothing doesn't suit you once it arrives. **[7]A further disadvantage** is that by shopping online you miss out on the high street experience, which, for many people, is a leisure activity. Going to the city centre with friends, trying on clothes and buying new things is much more fun than shopping at home by yourself.

[8]Overall, buying clothes online is obviously a useful way of adding to our wardrobes. However, there is still a place for the high-street shop.

b Read the essay again. Match phrases a–h to the phrases in bold in the essay (1–8) that have a similar meaning.

a one major problem _6_
b both problems and benefits to ___
c one major positive ___
d several problems with ___
e another benefit ___
f broadly speaking ___
g several benefits ___
h another drawback ___

I can …	Very well	Quite well	More practice
use verbs and dependent prepositions.	○	○	○
agree and disagree with someone.	○	○	○

12.5 Listening for pleasure

Scent branding

1 Match words and phrases 1–8 to a–h to make eight popular smells.

1	freshly baked		a	firewood
2	clean		b	coffee
3	freshly cut		c	flowers
4	a bunch of		d	after rain
5	freshly ground		e	bread
6	fresh air		f	grass
7	fish and		g	chips
8	burning		h	sheets

2 Read the dictionary definitions and choose the correct option to complete the statement below.

> **scent** /sent/ *noun* **1** [C,U] a pleasant smell: *This flower has no scent.*

> **brand** /brænd/ *noun* **1** [C] the name of a product that is made by a particular company: *a well-known brand of coffee*

Scent branding is …
a advertising perfumes.
b using a specific smell to advertise a company.
c adding chemicals to products to make them smell better.

3 **12.4**))) Listen to a presentation about scent branding.

4 Complete the summary below with the words and phrases in the box.

> explained   gave   remember   talk   t̶a̶l̶k̶e̶d̶   tell   told
> went on

> Anna Denman, from Scenting Inc, **1** _talked_ about scent branding, which is a way of marketing that uses the customers' sense of smell to help them **2**_____ a product or a company. She said that we remember 35% of what we smell, but only 5% of what we see, 2% of what we hear and 1% of what we touch. She **3**_____ us that her company provides equipment that pumps different smells into the air in shops. Ms Denman then **4**_____ that companies can choose a scent from their database, which has thousands of different options, or Scenting Inc can develop a specific smell for individual companies, called a 'signature scent'. She **5**_____ to **6**_____ us that this is used in shops and in a variety of products, such as candles, diffusers and beauty products. It can also be used in cards sent by mail or advertisements in magazines. Finally, she **7**_____ us a demonstration of the different packages available. It was a very informative **8**_____.

5 Would you use scent branding if you had a company of your own? Why/Why not?

Review: Units 11 and 12

Grammar

1   Report the sentences.

1   'I want to work in an advertising agency.'
Tim told me that he _wanted to work in an advertising_ _agency._

2   'I worked on a really exciting advertising campaign last year.'
Paula said that she _____

3   'We're hoping to start a new company next year.'
The managing director told us that they
_____

4   'How many employees do you have in your company?'
The tax inspector asked me _____

5   'Do you do any market research before launching a new product?'
Theo asked us _____

6   'What are you doing tomorrow?'
Tomas asked me _____

2   Complete the text with the correct form of the words in brackets. Use *would* or *should* if necessary.

☒   ─

Have you ever regretted downloading a file from a site that you didn't know much about? I have. And I ¹ _should have known_ (know) better. I ² _____ (not trust) a website that I knew so little about. In fact, when I clicked on the download icon, my internet service provider asked if I ³ _____ (want) to continue. That was where I went wrong. I ⁴_____ (cancel) the download immediately.

Now, I have a virus which is affecting some of my programs. I contacted my internet service provider, who, naturally, asked if I ⁵_____ (install) up-to-date antivirus software. I said no. This was really something that I ⁶_____ (do). It is also true that if I ⁷_____ (make) a backup, it ⁸_____ (not be) so bad. In the end, I had to shut down my system and take my PC to a specialist shop. I'm still waiting to see if they can repair the problem or if I have lost all my files.

Vocabulary

3   Choose the correct words to complete the sentences.

1   The *thief /*(victim)*/ outlaw* of a violent attack has just left hospital.

2   A bank *robber / thief / burglar* has left the country with over a million dollars.

3   The police have *arrested / suspected / escaped* a violent criminal and taken him to prison.

4   A gang of criminals have *sentenced / stolen / robbed* every shop in the high street.

5   Arthur Graham was sentenced *in / for / to* ten years in prison after being found guilty.

4   Match the two halves of the sentences.

1   Claire was very persuasive – she brought everybody _c_
2   The sales executive convinced us ___
3   I have to say that she really won us ___
4   Dani is successful and very good at getting ___
5   I just didn't agree – I didn't really see things ___
6   Stephanie managed to overcome ___

a   over with her knowledge of the subject.
b   her way at all.
c   round to her way of thinking.
d   all the objections to her plan.
e   her own way on most things.
f   to buy her product.

Speaking

5   Complete the sentences by adding the words in brackets in the correct position.

1   Could we move ᵒⁿ now, please? (on)
2   You admit this one looks much better. (must)
3   Are there other suggestions? (any)
4   That's what I was planning! (just)
5   I agree to a point. (up)
6   I couldn't more. (agree)

Audioscripts

Unit 1 Trends

Page 5, Exercise 4b

1.1 🔊

1

A Do you get on well with your neighbours?

B Not really. I don't even know their names!

2

A Do you have a lot in common with your partner?

B Yeah, we like the same music, books and lots of other things.

3

A When was the last time you had an argument with your best friend?

B Yesterday! But it was about something stupid, and we've already forgotten about it.

4

A How often do you meet up with your friends?

B Usually once a week, on Fridays.

5

A Do you make new friends easily?

B Yes, I'm very sociable. People think I'm crazy because I talk to everyone on the bus!

6

A How many old classmates do you keep in touch with?

B Maybe four or five, but just on Facebook.

Page 5, Exercise 7a

1.2 🔊

get on   I get_on well with her.

met up   I met_up with my mates yesterday.

Page 5, Exercises 7c & d

1.3 🔊

1 I make_an effort to get_in touch with distant relatives.
2 I have_a lot in common with_all my classmates.
3 Could you help_Adam_out?
4 I keep_in touch with_old friends.
5 I had_an argument with_an assistant.
6 It's_a shame you fell_out with_Alice.

Page 8, Exercise 4b

1.4 🔊

1 membership   5 employment
2 judgement   6 information
3 solution   7 friendship
4 celebrity

Page 9, Exercises 1a & b

1.5 🔊

How do you feel about the internet? Would life be better or worse without it? We asked people in the streets, and this is what they said:

1 Well, some people say that the internet causes a lot of problems, but personally, I think that it's an essential part of our lives now.
2 It's a terrible thing, if you ask me. All these young people tapping away on their mobiles all day long. Don't you think they're just wasting their lives?
3 I'm convinced that everybody's gone mad with this internet thing. Nobody can answer a simple question without checking it first online!
4 I definitely think that life is much better with the internet. It's hard to imagine what kind of life we would have without it!
5 I'm not much of an internet user myself, but as far as I'm concerned, it's got a lot more advantages than disadvantages.

Page 9, Exercise 3

1.6 🔊

M = Marion, **H** = Husband, **D** = Daughter, **S** = Son

M So, how do you feel about moving from Sydney to a smaller city?

H It's a great idea, if you ask me. This is the most expensive city in Australia, according to this article I've just read in the paper. Houses are the most expensive in the country, and we hardly ever eat out because it costs so much.

D That's true, but I really don't think we should move. All my friends live round here.

M You'll make new friends.

D Yes, but it isn't the same … What about school? Don't you think that schools in Sydney are better?

H I don't think that's true, actually. I'm sure there are good schools outside Sydney, too.

S It's OK, as far as I'm concerned … as long as the internet connection is good.

Page 9, Exercise 4a

1.7 🔊

1 As far as I'm concerned …
2 Some people say that …
3 I really feel that …
4 If you ask me …
5 How do you feel about …?
6 Don't you think …?

Page 9, Exercise 4b

1.8 🔊

1 As far as I'm concerned, I don't see why not.
2 Some people say that it's bad for you, but I'm not sure.
3 I really feel that you should stop smoking.
4 If you ask me, it's time to do something about it.
5 How do you feel about tests on animals?
6 Don't you think it's time to go home?

Unit 2 What a story!

Page 10, Exercise 2c

2.1 🔊

I = Interviewer, **S** = Safari guide, **W** = Window cleaner, **F** = Firefighter

I Do you think the animals recognize you?

S Sometimes I do. Once a lion got really close to me and looked me in the eye. I believe he knew exactly who I was.

I Do you believe anybody who likes cleaning could do your job?

W No way! Most people can't even go up a high ladder! But I wonder why people are so afraid of heights. With the right equipment, it's perfectly safe. And the view's fantastic!

I Have you ever realized that you were risking your life because you were too close to the heat?

F A lot of times. When I started, my colleagues always reminded me to stay at a safe distance.

I Should you always expect an animal to attack you, or are they less dangerous than they seem?

S Well, usually they're fine; but after some time, you learn to recognize the signs that they're stressed, like the way they walk or the sounds they make.

I Do you remember the first time you heard the alarm?

F Of course! It was my first day, and I wasn't expecting it – I didn't even have my uniform on!

I Do you ever have to remind the people inside the buildings that you are there?

W Yes! I usually make a noise or something. I remember once a couple were having a terrible argument, and when they saw me, they just kept going! It's none of my business, anyway.

I Do you ever wonder how they feel about all these visitors?

S Yes, but I try to make all the tourists realize that this is the animals' home, not ours!

Page 11, Exercise 3c

2.2 》

The best DVD ever

Barry McRoy likes movies, but he never thought that a DVD which a colleague had given him would save his life.

Fire and Rescue Director Barry McRoy was walking out of a restaurant one day when two men ran past him. They were fighting over a gun because they'd had an argument. One of them shot it and the bullet hit Barry in the chest. Luckily, he was carrying a DVD in his shirt pocket. A friend from work had recorded a TV programme for him the day before. Amazingly, he only realized what had happened while he was talking to the police, when he noticed a hole in his jacket.

Barry wasn't hurt, but the incident completely destroyed the DVD, which left him feeling a bit disappointed because he hadn't watched it yet!

Page 11, Exercises 5a & c

2.3 》

1 When I got home, my wife had cooked my favourite dish.
2 In my childhood, I had a dog called Spot.
3 At the end of the day, he was exhausted.
4 Thanks, I was looking all over the place for that!

5 Actually, we have enough time to get there.
6 They were good friends at school.

Page 12, Exercise 1b

2.4 》

On October 30, 1938, millions of New Yorkers had the shock of their lives while listening to the radio. The music was interrupted to announce an alien invasion. During the live broadcast, reporters interviewed people who had seen the aliens. As soon as the first part ended, thousands of people started calling the radio station and the police. Meanwhile, others went to the streets with their guns. What most people didn't find out until much later was that it was a hoax, an adaptation by director Orson Welles of a famous novel, *The War of the Worlds*. The radio station had actually announced this at the beginning of the broadcast, but many people were not paying attention. By the time the programme ended, there was general hysteria. It is estimated that over one million people actually believed the news was true.

Page 13, Exercise 8b

2.5 》

1	admitted	5	claimed
2	interviewed	6	mentioned
3	announced	7	informed
4	invented	8	reported

Page 14, Exercise 2a

2.6 》

1 Fortunately, it wasn't serious.
2 He said that, personally, he didn't mind.

Page 14, Exercise 2c

2.7 》

1 The accident was serious, but luckily, no one was hurt.
2 Unfortunately, there's nothing I can do about it.
3 I got the recipe wrong, but surprisingly, everybody loved the dish.
4 Amazingly, the magician reappeared at the back of the theatre.
5 They invested a lot in marketing, but interestingly, sales continued falling.

Page 15, Exercises 1 & 2b

2.8 》

1

A I heard this incredible story about a baby who fell from a high window on top of a man who was passing by. They both survived, fortunately.

B Really?

A Wait, that's not all. You're not going to believe this, but a year later the very same baby fell from the same window onto the very same man.

B How amazing! I don't know what's more unbelievable: the coincidence or how careless the baby's parents were!

2

A Someone told me about this incredible coincidence with an American writer. She was in a bookshop when she saw her favourite childhood book. She showed it to her husband, and when he opened it, her name was written inside. It was the exact copy she had as a child!

B That's incredible!

A Yes, especially considering she grew up in the USA and the bookshop was in Paris!

B What, you mean the book crossed the ocean and she still found it?

A Yeah, decades later.

B No way!

Page 15, Exercise 3a

2.9 》

1 Really?
2 How amazing!
3 That's awful!
4 What, you mean …?
5 No way!
6 You're joking!

Page 15, Exercise 3b

2.10 》

1 Really?
2 How amazing!
3 That's awful!
4 What, you mean …?
5 No way!
6 You're joking!

Unit 3 Life skills

Page 18, Exercise 2b

3.1 》

1 'I can resist everything except temptation.' *Oscar Wilde (Irish poet and playwright)*
2 'Writing is a form of therapy; sometimes I wonder how all those who do not write, compose or paint can manage to escape the madness … (of the) human condition.' *Graham Greene (English novelist)*

3 'It is no use saying, "We are doing our best". You have got to succeed in doing what is necessary.' *Winston Churchill (British politician)*

4 'The aim of the wise is not to secure pleasure, but to avoid pain.' *Aristotle (Greek philosopher)*

5 'Nothing makes me so happy as to observe nature and to paint what I see.' *Henri Rousseau (French painter)*

6 'Some are born great, some achieve greatness, and some have greatness thrust upon them.' *William Shakespeare (English playwright)*

Page 21, Exercises 6a & b

3.2))

1 You have to wear a shirt and tie.
2 You mustn't wear jeans.
3 You needn't start work at nine.
4 You can start at any time.

Page 23, Exercises 1a & b

3.3))

P = Presenter, **C** = Cathy

P On today's programme, I'm talking to environmental scientist Cathy Smith, who is going to show us how to make a solar cooker. Isn't that right, Cathy?

C Well, yes, absolutely. It's a really cheap and easy thing to do, too. In fact, most of us have probably got all the parts we need to make a solar cooker in our kitchens and garages.

P I can see that because you've brought all the bits and pieces needed into the studio. I can see two large cardboard boxes, another large piece of cardboard, an old newspaper, lots of aluminium foil, a piece of glass, and black paint.

C Yes, that's about it.

P OK. So, how do you make the cooker?

C OK. Let me show you. Notice that I have two cardboard boxes and one is larger than the other one.

P OK.

C The first thing you do is place this larger box in front of you, and put lots of pieces of newspaper in the bottom of it.

P Can you show me?

C Sure. You do it like this.

P Ah, OK, so you're making balls out of the newspaper and putting them in the box.

C That's right.

P Why?

C Well, this is insulation. It's so that the box will stay hot.

P OK.

C When you've done this, use the black paint to paint the inside of the smaller box, just the bottom of the box. Make sure it's completely black.

P OK.

C After doing this, cover the sides of the box with the aluminium foil. OK?

P I see, yes. So, now there is aluminium foil inside the small box, on each side, and on the bottom there is black paint.

C That's right.

P OK, what next?

C Put the smaller box inside the larger box, and attach a large piece of aluminium foil to make a solar dish. Place the piece of glass over the large box, and put your solar cooker in the sun. Heat from the sun should make the inside of the smaller box really hot. All you have to do is put some food in the box, and it'll cook.

P Wow, that's amazing. I can see one problem, though. We're in England. So, where are we going to get any sun?

Unit 4 Space

Page 25, Exercise 5b

4.1))

Next week, on Travel the World, I'm going to visit an unspoilt island in the Pacific, where islanders face a difficult choice. A major hotel chain has offered a lot of money to build a luxury hotel, and they're going to start construction next year. At least, that's their plan. The islanders have the final say, and they're going to hold a meeting to discuss all the issues. We hope to be there to hear what they think. Currently, nobody knows what they'll decide to do. Many people believe that tourism will bring unwanted pollution and large, ugly buildings to the island. At the same time, others believe it will create jobs and introduce shops and services. On other islands nearby, for example, the arrival of tourism has resulted in the destruction of coral reefs and the islanders' traditional way of life; but people are richer and have more opportunities. Clearly, the choice isn't an easy one. I'll see you next week. Goodbye from paradise.

Page 27, Exercise 6b

4.2))

1 Over a quarter of a million people will definitely join our celebration this year.
2 We are likely to plant more trees than ever before.
3 Our forests will definitely not survive unless we plant more trees.
4 Over two hundred school and community groups will possibly take part in this year's event.
5 You probably won't need them, but our team of volunteers are here to help.
6 National Tree Week is unlikely to succeed without the help of people like you!

Page 29, Exercises 1a & b

4.3))

Conversation 1

A Hello, sir. How can I help you?
B Er … I really like these black ones. I wonder whether you have them in my size.
A OK. I'll go and have a look for you.
B Thanks for your help, I really appreciate it. I'm size 44, by the way.
A OK. I'll be back in a minute.

Conversation 2

A Hello. Town centre, please.
B Sorry, this is the number 6. You need the 68 for the town centre, mate.
A Ah, could you tell me when the 68 leaves?
B They're every fifteen minutes, so there'll be one along soon. Can I help you with anything else?
A No, that's great, thanks. I'll just wait here, then.

Conversation 3

A Hello, National Bank.
B Oh, hello. I wonder if you could help me transfer £30,000 to my new account?
A Certainly, Madam. Could I just check some details first?
B Of course.
A What's your full name and address?

Conversation 4

A Er … hello. I have an appointment with Miss Lynn.
B OK. Please take a seat in the waiting room.
A Over here? OK. Will she be long?
B No, I don't think so, but are you aware that you're late? Your appointment was at 2.15.
A Oh, really, I'm sorry. Will I have to wait longer then?

B No, as I said, it won't be long.

A OK. Just one last question. It cost me £80 last time. How much do you think it'll cost this time?

B I really don't know, Madam. You'll have to ask Miss Lynn.

Page 29, Exercise 2b

4.4)))

R How can I help you?

G I wonder if you could give me a wake-up call at 7?

R Certainly. Are you aware that breakfast starts at 8 tomorrow because it's Sunday?

G No, thanks for telling me. OK. Could you wake me at 7.30, then?

R Certainly. Can I help you with anything else?

G Could you tell me when the bus goes to the airport?

R Yes, of course. The airport bus leaves at 10 a.m., 12, 2 and 4.

G OK. Thanks for your help – I appreciate it.

Page 30, Exercise 2

4.5)))

P = Presenter, **S** = Sarah

P When we think of churches and cathedrals, we think of large buildings made of stone and glass, buildings which appear to be ancient and permanent. On today's programme, however, we're going to discuss the work of a Japanese architect who builds churches and cathedrals which are modern and temporary, and, believe it or not, made almost entirely of recycled paper. Here to tell us more is Sarah Hillyard, from the online magazine, *Architect*. Hello, Sarah, and welcome to the programme.

S Hello. Thank you for inviting me.

P So, paper cathedrals? I find it hard to believe that such buildings are possible.

S Well, paper is an extremely useful building material. It's inexpensive and can be very strong. That's why Tokyo-based architect Shigeru Ban started developing it as a building material back in the 1980s. He found that paper tubing was perfect for building walls, ceilings and roofs.

P What do you mean by paper tubing?

S Well, imagine the tube of cardboard inside a roll of toilet paper or kitchen paper. Then imagine that it's really thick and three or four metres long. You can make a wonderful column with a thick, long cardboard tube. And if you connect a number of tubes together, you can make the frame of a building.

P I see. But what's the point of making a paper or cardboard building that isn't going to last all that long?

S OK. Well, Shigeru Ban has become known as the 'disaster architect', and for good reason. His architecture is perfect in a disaster zone. In fact, his work became famous when he came up with a solution to the desperate need for shelters in refugee camps in the early 1990s. Refugees who have lost their homes often don't have enough wood to build shelters. Ban's solution was to make shelters from paper tubing, and it was perfect. The shelters were cheap, strong, easy to build, and they saved lives.

P So, how did Shigeru Ban go from building shelters to building cathedrals?

S Well, in 1995, an enormous earthquake destroyed hundreds of buildings in the city of Kobe in Japan. It was a terrible catastrophe and more than 6,000 people died. Ban designed many of the temporary shelters for people made homeless by the earthquake, but he was also asked to build a church to replace the Takatori Catholic Church because it had been so badly damaged.

P So, he designed a church from paper tubes?

S Yes. It was called the Paper Dome, and it stood in Kobe for ten years. Then there was an earthquake in Taiwan and the people of Kobe decided to give the Paper Dome to the people of Taiwan. They took the Dome apart and rebuilt it in Taiwan, where you can see it today.

P How amazing. After that, every time there is a disaster, I guess people think of Ban and ask him to help.

S I suppose you could say that. It led to his most famous design. In 2011, there was a major earthquake in the city of Christchurch in New Zealand and its cathedral was badly damaged. Ban was invited to build a temporary replacement, the Cardboard Cathedral. It's over twenty metres high and can hold seven hundred people.

P And it's still standing?

S Oh, yes. It's one of Christchurch's best-loved sites. If you're ever in New Zealand, try to visit it.

Unit 5 Entertainment

Page 34, Exercises 4b & c

5.1)))

1 wonderful, violent
2 enjoyable, original
3 surprising, amusing
4 disappointing, entertaining

Page 36, Exercise 1b

5.2)))

1
A Were you very tired after the race?
B Tired? We were absolutely exhausted!

2
A Ooh, this tomato sauce is really tasty.
B It's more than tasty. It's absolutely delicious!

3
A Brrr! It's a bit too cold for me in here.
B I know. It's absolutely freezing!

4
A It's a really big house. It has eighteen bedrooms.
B It's more than big. It's absolutely enormous!

5
A The horror film was very scary!
B Yes! It was absolutely terrifying!

6
A She's really clever and got As in all her exams.
B I think she's absolutely brilliant!

7
A It's raining again. The weather's been really bad this month.
B It's rained every day! The weather's been absolutely terrible!

8
A I didn't expect her to win the contest. The result was very surprising.
B Surprising?! It was absolutely astonishing!

Page 36, Exercise 1c

5.3)))

1 We were absolutely exhausted!
2 It's absolutely delicious!
3 It's absolutely freezing!
4 It's absolutely enormous!
5 It was absolutely terrifying!
6 I think she's absolutely brilliant!
7 The weather's been absolutely terrible!
8 It was absolutely astonishing!

Page 37, Exercises 1a & b

5.4)))

A Have you seen *Empire* magazine's list of their top five films?

B No, I haven't. Not yet. Let me have a look ... Mmm. It's not a very original list, is it, Adam? I expected it to be less predictable, but it isn't really. These are all just well-known popular Hollywood films.

A Well, yes, but they're all classic films, aren't they? They're all worth seeing.

B Well, I've only seen *Star Wars* and *Raiders of the Lost Ark*. I haven't seen any of the others, so I wouldn't know.

A Unbelievable. You haven't seen *The Godfather*?

B No. Is it any good?

A It's amazing. It's set in New York and it's about a mafia family. It lasts over two hours. I'd recommend you download it as soon as you can.

B Over two hours? I'm not at all sure about that. It sounds very dull.

A You're joking! It's a classic. It's definitely in my top two films, but I don't think it should be number one. It's nothing like as good as *The Shawshank Redemption*. Now, that's an even better film. It's really worth seeing.

B Is it a comedy?

A Well, no, it's about two men who are in prison for life.

B Well, that doesn't sound very entertaining.

A It's only the greatest film ever made. It's better than *The Godfather*, and much better than *Jaws*. *Jaws* is good, though. I'd recommend you watch it one of these days. I think you'd like it.

B OK. What about the films I've seen, *Star Wars* and *Raiders of the Lost Ark*?

A Well, they're alright, but not as good as the other three films on the list. They're quite ordinary, really. Harrison Ford stars in both of them, of course, and his performances are great. In my opinion, *Raiders of the Lost Ark* is better than *Star Wars*. They're enjoyable films, and popular classics, I suppose, but I wouldn't really recommend either of them.

Page 37, Exercise 2b

5.5)))

1

A I think *Batman Returns* is the greatest film of all time.

B Mmm ... I'm not at all sure about that.

2

A Are you disappointed by this film?

B Yes, I am. It's nothing like as good as I thought it would be.

3

A I haven't seen *City of God* yet.

B Really? It's worth seeing, you know.

Unit 6 In control?

Page 38, Exercises 2a & b

6.1)))

1	motorway	4	overtake
2	injured	5	driverless
3	accident		

Page 41, Exercise 5b

6.2)))

1

A Why don't you wear that green necklace any more?

B Unfortunately, I've lost it.

2

A Where's Jo?

B Outside. She's been working in the garden all day. And she's still out there now.

3

A Are you and Louise friends?

B Yes. We've known each other for ages.

4

A Sarah seems happier these days. Why's that?

B Well, she's been doing better at school recently. I hope it continues.

5

A Do you know Carl well?

B Not really. I've only met him twice.

6

A I haven't seen Ana at the sports centre for ages. What has she been doing?

B Actually, she's broken her arm.

Page 42, Exercises 4a & b

6.3)))

1 stressful, cheerful, social, careless, lucky

2 reliable, traditional, acceptable, enjoyable

3 personal, comfortable, typical, practical, sociable

Page 42, Exercise 5

6.4)))

1 I prefer furniture that is traditional and comfortable.

2 I feel nervous in stressful situations.

3 It was a reliable and successful company.

4 Don't ask personal questions in social situations.

Page 43, Exercises 1a & b

6.5)))

T = Tom, **K** = Kerry

T Hello.

K Hi, Tom. It's Kerry. How are you?

T I'm fine, fine ... Hope you're still on for Saturday?

K Ah, well, that's why I was ringing. I'm afraid there's been a change of plan. My parents are coming over on Saturday ... for dinner. We made the arrangement ages ago, but I forgot. I'm really sorry. We'll have to eat out another night.

T Oh, OK. That's a shame. I'd booked a table at Mario's. I was really looking forward to it.

K I'm sorry. How about going another night? Friday?

T Friday? Mmm ... Let me see. No, I can't make it then.

K Oh, OK.

T Yeah. I've got something else on. Football practice. How about a week on Saturday? Not this Saturday, but the following Saturday.

K Hang on a second. Yeah ... That's fine with me.

T Great. Well, enjoy dinner with your parents. I'll get back to you later in the week, and we'll decide where to meet. OK?

K Yeah. Great! See you soon. Bye, Tom.

T Bye.

Unit 7 Ambitions

Page 47, Exercise 7a

7.1)))

used to   I used to go to work by bus

they'd   they'd go to work by bus

Page 47, Exercise 7b

7.2)))

1 I used to work at home.

2 I'd go by car every day. I never walked.

3 I used a copy from the Web.

4 I'd travel abroad a lot.

Page 47, Exercise 7c

7.3 》》)

1   I used to work at home.
    I use it to work at home.
2   I'd go by car every day. I never walked.
    I go by car every day. I never walk.
3   I used a copy from the Web.
    I used to copy from the Web.
4   I'll travel abroad a lot.
    I'd travel abroad a lot.

Page 49, Exercise 5b

7.4 》》)

A   Today's call-in is about the book *The Art of Doing*, and our first caller, Matt, is on the line. Matt, how many self-help books have you read?
B   Not many, but I've read a lot of biographies of well-known politicians.
A   Who told you about *The Art of Doing*?
B   My boss mentioned it in a training session on career achievements.
A   Do you remember where you bought it?
B   Yes, I usually buy books at a store in the city centre, but I got this one online.
A   And can I ask which your favourite chapter was?
B   My mother's Brazilian, so it was the chapter on how Hélio Castroneves became a racing champion.
A   What changed in your life after reading this book?
B   Well, not much so far, but I definitely feel more determined.
A   Who would you recommend this book to?
B   Mm ... To anybody who wants to achieve more in life, I guess.

Page 51, Exercises 1 & 2a

7.5 》》)

I = Interviewer, J = James
I   Good morning, and thanks for coming again.
J   Good morning.
I   So, when you came in to see us a couple of weeks ago, you'd applied for the position of Assistant Marketing Manager.
J   Yes, that's right.
I   OK. Right. Well, due to some unexpected events, we have another possibility we'd like to discuss with you.
J   I'm not sure I understand. Do you mean you're offering me another job?
I   Well, yes ... yes, that's right. You see, our Public Relations Manager has had to leave us, quite suddenly, and your CV fits the job description perfectly. So the job's yours! If you're interested, of course.

J   Initially, very interested indeed, but could you tell me more about the job? Is there a job description I could look at?
I   Yes, of course. Your responsibilities would include dealing with journalists and managing our pages on social networks. It is a position that requires a certain amount of quick thinking.
J   I see. Could you give me some examples of that?
I   Well, for instance, press conferences. I'm sure you've read all the bad news about us recently. There have been a lot of difficult questions. So, what do you think?
J   Hmm, let me think ... Well, I really like Public Relations and it is for a managerial position, so yes, I'm more than happy to take it!
I   Excellent! I hope you're available to start immediately, there are some pressing ...

Page 51, Exercise 3a

7.6 》》)

Conversation 1

Ja = James, Jo = Journalist
Ja   I'm afraid Mr Clarkson is not available any more, but I'm in charge of PR now, and I'm happy to answer your questions.
Jo   'Not available'? Could you explain what you mean? Is this related to the recent scandal?
Ja   No, it isn't. He doesn't work here any longer, but I'm afraid I can't comment on the reasons. Next question!

Conversation 2

J = James, M = Marie
J   OK, so now I've met all of you, I'd like to talk about our image. I think we need something new and fresh. Any suggestions?
M   I'm not sure I understand ...
J   Let me give you an example ... OK, let me think ... Right. This logo. How long have you had this logo?

Unit 8 Choices

Page 52, Exercise 2b

8.1 》》)

1   I was really pleased when my company started to offer childcare. It really changed my life because now I can spend much more time with my son.
2   I know this sounds awful, but it was when my neighbour moved out last month! He was so noisy and the walls are really thin.

3   I've only been living in the capital for three months, and it's been really hard to get used to the pollution. My eyes really burn sometimes.
4   I watched a documentary on global poverty last week. It really breaks your heart to see that so many have so little.
5   Last holidays, I worked for two weeks as a volunteer in an old people's home. The old people were fantastic, and I learnt so much from them.

Page 53, Exercise 5a

8.2 》》)

If you meditate, you'll feel happy.
You'll feel happy if you meditate.

Page 53, Exercise 5b

8.3 》》)

a   if you want happiness for a lifetime
b   you will be successful
c   you'll never enjoy the sunshine
d   if you can't love and respect yourself
e   you are too busy
f   you will never be happy

Page 53, Exercises 5c & d

8.4 》》)

a   If you want happiness for a lifetime, help someone else. (Chinese proverb)
b   If you love what you are doing, you will be successful. (Herman Cain)
c   You'll never enjoy the sunshine if you spend your whole life waiting for the storm. (Morris West)
d   If you can't love and respect yourself, no one else will be able to make that happen. (Stacey Charter)
e   If you are too busy to laugh, you are too busy. (proverb)
f   You will never be happy if you continue to search for what happiness consists of. (Albert Camus)

Page 55, Exercise 5b

8.5 》》)

S = Sonya, L = Li
S   The first one's easy. I'd definitely tell the shop assistant.
L   Me, too. It actually happened to me once. Hmm ... What's next? I think I'd confess my mistake to my boss, even if I hated the guy.
S   I don't know, that's a hard one. But this one's not: I'd never do a parachute jump, even if they gave me £1,000,000!
L   Really? Well, I'd jump today if I had the chance. And for free!
S   Not for me, thanks! What about this one, about the animal? What would you do?

L I have to admit I wouldn't risk my life, unless it was my own pet.

S I guess, but I think I'd try to save any animal if I didn't have to risk my own life.

L Well, I suppose we haven't done too badly, have we?

Page 57, Exercise 1

8.6))

A Hello, everyone. I'm Isabelle and hmm ... I'm here to talk to you about ... about ... distractions. I'm going to tell you about the main distractions ... no, first I'm going to ... hmm ... explain hmm ...

B So we've looked at the main distractions around us, which were alerts on your mobile, colleagues and outside noises, and then ...

C Good morning, my name's Rashid and I'm going to talk about choices. Have you noticed how many choices we have around us? Is that good or bad? How can we deal better with so many choices? ...

D Let's move on now to look at the third and last thing you can do to deal with choices. It's actually about what to do after you've made one. Once you've made up your mind ...

Page 57, Exercises 2a & c

8.7))

A Hello, everyone. I'm Isabelle and I'm here to talk to you about distractions. Firstly, I'm going to explain why there are so many distractions around us. Then, I'm going to tell you about the three main distractions we have to deal with, and finally I'm also going to suggest ways of staying focused. OK?

B So we've looked at the main distractions around us, which were colleagues, outside noises and alerts on your mobile, and then we saw strategies to stay focused. Now I'd like to finish with a phrase from ...

C Good morning, my name's Rashid and I'm going to talk about choices. Have you noticed how many choices we have around us? Is that good or bad? How can we deal better with so many choices?

D Let's move on now to look at the third and last thing you can do to deal with choices. It's actually about what to do after you've made one. Once you've made up your mind, stop thinking about the other options immediately and be happy with what you chose.

Page 57, Exercise 4

8.8))

Hello, everyone. I'm Isabelle, and I'm here to talk to you about distractions. Firstly, I'm going to explain why there are so many distractions around us. Then, I'm going to tell you about the three main distractions we have to deal with, and finally I'm also going to suggest ways of staying focused. OK?

We live in a world which is going faster day by day. Everything is urgent, and, because we are connected 24 hours a day, we feel the need to answer everybody and everything immediately. However, this can be a disaster for your work or studies.

Firstly, if people around you often distract you, tell them politely that you are a bit busy now, and suggest discussing it over coffee or lunch later. I'm sure they'll understand.

Secondly, external noises. These are more difficult to deal with, because you just can't ask them to stop. You will find, though, that if you put up curtains, you won't be *looking* outside, so the noise won't be such a problem.

And finally, those constant alerts on your mobile. But this is the easiest to solve: just turn off the sound! Then you can ...

Now I'd like to finish with a phrase from Tom Kite, an American professional golfer: 'You'll always find a distraction if you're looking for one.' Are there any questions?

Page 58, Exercise 2

8.9))

P = Presenter, **D** = Danny

P Most of us accept that we live in a modern consumer society, and that if we want to eat we have to pay for our food. But have you ever considered whether it would be possible to survive in an urban environment if you didn't want to spend any money – if you wanted to eat for free? Well, this week, I met up with Danny Clark, a man who belongs to a community who believe that we shouldn't have to pay for food. I began by asking Danny when he started living without money.

D I joined the community about eighteen months ago, and I haven't spent a penny since. People probably think we're starving, or living on handouts, or begging in the streets. But it couldn't be further from the truth. There is plenty of food out there if you know where to look.

P Really? I wouldn't know where to find food if I couldn't go down to my local supermarket or corner shop.

D Well, if you live in the middle of a town, your local shop is probably a good place to start. Shops are constantly throwing away perfectly good food because their food always has to be of a very high quality – it has to look good, too. If you told them that you'd be happy to take away any of their food that they couldn't sell because it didn't look perfect, they'd probably say yes.

P Or they might tell you to go away.

D Well, yes, that's possible. But actually most shopkeepers feel guilty about throwing away food. Usually, they'll let you have it. We're eating food that would otherwise be wasted.

P OK. I see. That's a good point. How else do you get food?

D Well, I get most of my food from foraging. That means finding food that is growing in the wild. Berries and mushrooms, for example, and if you live near the coast, seaweed is a fantastic food. Sadly, I'm too far from the sea to be able to eat that, but there are loads of different herbs and leaves out there, too. Being vegetarian, I can find most of the food I need in woods.

P But you can't just live on mushrooms and berries.

D Well, some of my friends grow their own food in their gardens, or even in window boxes if they have flats. I have no idea why more people don't grow their own. And I barter for food with friends. I'll swap food that I've found for food that they've grown.

P OK. But why do you do this? Why would you choose this lifestyle?

D Well. Firstly, I think we waste too much food. It is terrible that we fill up our bins with food that we could have eaten, and terrible that supermarkets throw food away. By choosing to live without paying for food, I am showing people how much wasted food there is out there, and encouraging people not to waste food themselves.

P And secondly?

D Well, secondly, I really enjoy my lifestyle. I've built up good relationships with people I barter with for food, I love finding food in the countryside, and, of course, I live much more cheaply than most people. Eating for free is fun. You should try it!

Unit 9 Appearances

Page 62, Exercises 3a & b
9.1))

1 historical	5 modern
2 colourful	6 traditional
3 detailed	7 old-fashioned
4 mysterious	

Page 63, Exercise 5b
9.2))

1 She must be a secret millionaire!
2 It can't be real!
3 What reason could she have?
4 The painting could have a special significance.
5 Turner might be her great-grandfather.
6 It can't be there by accident.
7 You must be really bored.
8 There must be a really big hole in the wall.

Page 65, Exercises 1a & b
9.3))

A = Anna, G = Greg

A Hi Greg. You look upset. Are you OK?
G Well, yes, yes. Look. Sorry to bother you, but there's something I'm not happy about.
A Oh, really, I'm sorry about that. What's the problem?
G Well, I'm waking up in the middle of the night, every night, night after night. I know that it sounds mean to ask you to keep Jenny quiet, but it can't go on like this. The problem's been going on for weeks.
A OK. But what are we supposed to do about it? I mean, she's only two months old, you know. It's what children of that age do, isn't it? They keep waking up and crying in the middle of the night. Do you want us to send her away, or put her in a box? She isn't a dog, you know, we can't put her at the far end of the garden or anything.
G Well, yes, but maybe you could move her to another room, you know, further away from my bedroom wall.
A What? Into the living room? Or the kitchen? Look, Greg, there really isn't another room we can move her into. And, anyway, you aren't exactly the quietest of neighbours. You know we hear your music late at night quite often, and we never complain.
G Oh, OK. Well, I didn't know that. I'll make sure I turn the volume down. But do you think you could do something about the noise? I'm not getting much sleep.
A Well, I hear you, Greg, but there's nothing we can do about it, is there? She'll grow out of it, you know. Until then, wear earplugs. Goodbye, Greg.
G Goodbye … Some people are so selfish …

Page 65, Exercises 2a & b
9.4))

1 Do you think you could turn your music down?
2 Your dog's barking keeps waking me up.
3 Sorry to bother you, but your rubbish bin is in front of our house.
4 The problem's been going on for months!
5 I'm sorry about that. I'll make sure it's quiet tomorrow.

Unit 10 Compete and cooperate

Page 66, Exercise 3
10.1))

1 set up a business
2 give a guarantee
3 raise a million
4 meet an investor
5 short of cash

Page 69, Exercises 5a & b
10.2))

1 lose a match
2 win an Olympic medal
3 break the record
4 take part in the Olympics

Page 71, Exercise 1
10.3))

G = Greeter, O = Omar, L = Louisa

G Is this your first time at the event?
O Yes, it is.
L Yes. We can't wait. What would you recommend we go and see?
G Well, I'd definitely recommend watching the March of Nations. That starts in half an hour in the main stadium here. And then the American football tournament starts.
O That sounds great. We really want to see that.
L Yeah.
G After that it depends on which sports you enjoy. I suggest that you look at the timetable. Choose your favourite sports and go from there.
O OK. Thank you, that's a great suggestion.
L Yes, thanks.
G Oh, and don't forget, this afternoon, many of the indoor events start. There's tae kwon do and table tennis, and don't miss the basketball tournament.
L OK. Tae kwon do? What do you think, Omar?
O Well, we could watch that, but I'm a basketball fan and we can't watch everything.
L Oh, OK. Basketball it is, then.
G It's very popular. It might be a good idea to buy a ticket in advance for that. The wrestling is really popular, too, and the finals are the day after tomorrow. Have you thought of going to the wrestling tournament?
O Well, that's a good idea, but we have to leave then, I'm afraid.
G Ah …
L Yeah. That's a real shame. Ah well, another time, maybe. Right, let's find our seats for the March of Nations.

Page 71, Exercises 2a & b
10.4))

1 I'd definitely recommend watching the March of Nations.
2 Don't miss the basketball tournament.
3 It might be a good idea to buy a ticket in advance for that.
4 Thank you, that's a great suggestion.
5 That sounds great!
6 That's a good idea, but we have to leave then.

Unit 11 Consequences

Page 74, Exercise 3b
11.1))

1 They were sentenced at 3 p.m. today.
2 She was robbed.
3 He was suspected of murder.
4 Two prisoners escaped.
5 I was arrested by the police.

Page 75, Exercise 6a
11.2))

… probably have escaped.
… they'd probably have escaped.
… hadn't shot anyone, they'd probably have escaped.
If they hadn't shot anyone, they'd probably have escaped.

Page 75, Exercise 6b
11.3))

1 They might have lived longer if they'd stopped committing crimes.
2 Bonnie probably wouldn't have been shot if she hadn't stayed with Clyde.

Page 76, Exercises 3a & b
11.4))

1 nasty	insult	victim
2 criticize	passionate	unpleasant
3 regret	bully	careless
4 blogging	issue	upset

Page 77, Exercises 5b & c
11.5))

1 She should have spoken up.
2 They shouldn't have criticized other celebrities.
3 Should he have been so critical?
4 He shouldn't have sent that nasty tweet.
5 You should have been more careful.
6 Shouldn't you be studying for your exams?

Page 79, Exercises 1a & b
11.6))
Conversation 1

A OK. Could we move on? There is one more thing we have to discuss before the end of the break, and that's punctuality. Too many students are arriving late for lectures, especially in the mornings. I think we should do something about it.
B You're right. I'm convinced that we need to be a lot stricter. It interrupts the lecture and other students are unhappy about that. Perhaps we should send late-comers home. You know, stop them from coming in.
A OK. Another option would be to fine them. You must admit that the problem would soon be solved if they had to pay ten euros every time they were more than five minutes late.
B Mmm. I'm not sure we could fine them. But I do think we should have been stricter in the past, so perhaps it's about time we started doing something about it. We could ask late students to wait outside. They wouldn't be able to come into the lecture theatre until the break.
C I think that's a good idea.
A OK. So, we've decided that we will have a strict policy of banning students from the lecture theatre until after the break if they're late.
B Yes.
A That's settled, then. I think we should announce this as soon as we can.
Conversation 2
A Right. It's almost two o'clock. We're running out of time. What else are we not happy about?

B The cafeteria. It isn't open before lectures start, which is really annoying.
A OK. But let's leave that for now. We're here to talk about lectures, not facilities. Is there anything else we should discuss with Dr Harris?
C Well, I don't see why lectures should start so early. Lots of students don't live on campus, and have to travel in. I think 9.30 or even 10.00 would be a better time. Don't you think that more students would come to lectures if they weren't so early?
B You're right. The traffic is really busy before nine.
C It would definitely be easier for everyone to come in later.
B Absolutely.
A OK. So, what we're saying is that we want a later start?
B Yep.
C I think so.
A Are there any other suggestions?
B No. That's all. Actually, I think we'd better get going. It's past two now.

Page 79, Exercise 2b
11.7))
Conversation 3

C = Chairperson, S1 = Student representative, S2 = Staff representative
C OK. That's decided. Could we move on? The next item on the agenda is lunch times. Should they be longer?
S1 In our opinion, they should be longer. You must admit that students work harder when they've had a good long break and plenty to eat.
S2 I'm not so sure. A longer lunchtime means a late finish to the day, and students get tired late in the day.
C OK. Well, a late finish is just one possibility. Another option would be an earlier start.
S1 That's a good idea. An earlier start and a longer lunchtime.
S2 I agree.
C OK. That's settled, then. We'll start lectures at the college thirty minutes earlier.

Unit 12 Influence

Page 80, Exercises 2a & b
12.1))

1 billboard	amusing	slogan
2 memorable	advert	persuasive
3 product	confusing	clever
4 effective	logo	poster

Page 82, Exercises 2a & b
12.2))

1 I won them‿over.
2 He got his‿own way.
3 They brought‿us round to their way‿of thinking.
4 She saw‿it my way.

Page 85, Exercises 1a & b
12.3))
Conversation 1

SC = Senior copywriter, JC = Junior copywriter
SC Well, I think that women want to look stylish and professional in the office. Don't you agree?
JC Absolutely! That's just what I was thinking.
SC So, that's why I thought of the slogan 'Look Smart, Feel Smart' for this product. What's your view?
JC I couldn't agree more. The message we want to get across is that if you want to wear one of these instead of trousers, say, you'll be both fashionable and powerful. I think it's a great slogan.

Conversation 2

Co = Copywriter, Cl = Client
Co There was a time when advertising luxury products, like jewellery and watches, was all about appealing to people's dreams of living like a movie star.
Cl Mmm. Well, yes, I suppose so.
Co But, today, society is very different. The men who wear your products don't want to feel like stars any more. They just want to be ordinary guys who live ordinary lives.
Cl Er … well, I'm not sure about that. Our products are worn by royalty, you know. And they're beautifully manufactured with many moving parts.
Co Well, yes, I was just going to say that. They're outstanding products. Outstanding products for ordinary people. That's how we're going to sell them. And we've asked comedian Tommy Lloyd to be the face on the posters. Don't you think he'll appeal to your customers?
Cl Well, no, I totally disagree. The man's a fool. It'll be a disaster.

Conversation 3

M = Manager, C1 = Copywriter 1,
C2 = Copywriter 2

M Right. Let's see what ideas you've got for Gleam. Remember, it's a new product but the manufacturer is one of our oldest clients, so we have to get this right.

C1 Well, we think a product like this is partly about freshness and great taste, but it's also about whether it works or not. We thought we'd try to sell it by getting a leading dentist to say how good it is.

M Yes, but I can't help thinking that every brand tries to do that. That doesn't seem very original.

C2 That's a good point. However, we've already done some research and found out that, in scientific tests, Gleam is found to be more effective than any other product on the market. It has extra fluoride, you see.

C1 I was just going to say that. Scientifically, it's the best. Wouldn't you say that we should use that evidence in our campaign?

M You might be right. OK. Let's use that idea. Go and call this dentist, and start thinking of ideas for the poster campaign.

Page 86, Exercise 3

12.4))

A OK, listen up everybody. As you know, we're looking for new ways to advertise our brand, so we asked Ms Anna Denman, from Scenting Inc, to come here and explain this concept, umm, this new idea to us. Thank you for coming, Ms Denman.

B Good morning, and thank you so much for having me here. OK, you're all here? … Great. Then I'll start. OK, I'm going to talk about scent branding with you today.

When was the last time you smelled something that brought back a pleasant memory? Maybe the perfume your mother used to wear, or the cookies your grandmother used to bake. It's interesting, isn't it? As soon as that scent hits you, places, people and events come back to you. Things you probably haven't thought about for ages. That's the type of experience I'm here to talk about today. So what is scent branding and how do we use it?

Scent branding is using a specific smell to make your customers remember your company. Why? Because it is proved that we remember 35% of what we smell, compared to only 5% of what we see, 2% of what we hear, and 1% of what we touch.

Let me explain how it works. Once we've chosen the best scent for your company, we provide equipment that pumps it into the air in your shops. Customers will then associate that smell with your brand, and will recognize it whenever they smell it again. So …

C I have a question. Apart from helping our customers remember our brand, can a scent do anything else like, say, make people spend more money?

B Excellent question! Yes, there are different scents for different purposes. Shops usually want a smell that encourages customers to open their wallets and spend some money, but hotels may want a type of scent that make their guests feel at home, and banks need something that relaxes their clients while they're waiting.

So, how do you choose a scent for your brand? Well, we have a database with thousands of different scents to choose from.

But if you prefer something more exclusive, we can also develop a unique scent for your company. That's called a 'signature scent'. Hugo Boss, Burger King, Thompson Hotels, Abercrombie & Fitch, The Bellagio casino … they all have their signature scents, which they use in a variety of ways.

D If I can just interrupt here …?

B Of course.

D Don't people feel tricked when they realize that what they're smelling is an artificial fragrance, designed to persuade them to spend money?

B Well, that's the great thing about it. Quite often, customers aren't even aware of the smell, but even when we tell them about it, they're usually surprised and curious, never annoyed.

A Going back to what you were saying … how exactly could a company use their scent for marketing?

B Well, there are a number of products you can sell or give to your customers with your signature scent: candles, diffusers (you know, those little bottles with sticks in them that you put around your house), beauty products … You can also send cards by mail with your signature scent, you can publish perfumed ads in magazines, there are many possibilities!

Does anybody else have a question? Well, let's move on to our packages, shall we?

Answer key

Unit 1 Trends

1.1 Are you really my friend? page 4

Grammar present simple, continuous and perfect

1 1 *has grown*
   2 access
   3 is still changing
   4 check
   5 is increasing
   6 have already uploaded
   7 is currently growing
   8 has
   9 have just checked

2 1 *yet*
   2 all the time
   3 already
   4 at the moment
   5 now
   6 every time

3 1 *Have you heard*
   2 is increasing
   3 has
   4 check
   5 use
   6 has already visited
   7 include
   8 are taking place

Vocabulary friendship

4a 1 c 2 f 3 a 4 d 5 e 6 b

5 1 I fell *out* with my partner once because of football.
   2 My parents helped me out when I didn't have enough money.
   3 I get on well with everybody from work.
   4 I'm terrible at getting in touch with distant relatives.
   5 I met up with people from work to celebrate a birthday last week.

6 1 *keep*   4 have
   2 help   5 make
   3 trust

7b 1 consonant
    2 vowel

7c 1 *I make an effort to get in touch with distant relatives.*
    2 I have a lot in common with all my classmates.

3 Could you help Adam out?
4 I keep in touch with old friends.
5 I had an argument with an assistant.
6 It's a shame you fell out with Alice.

1.2 Why spending's #trending page 6

Vocabulary spending

1 a 2 b 4 c 1 d 3

2 1 *items*
   2 discount
   3 two for the price of one
   4 customer
   5 half-price
   6 deals

3 1 *a* 2 a 3 b 4 b 5 c 6 b
   7 c 8 a 9 c

Grammar state verbs

4 1 *believe*   4 seems
   2 owned   5 understand
   3 tastes

5 1 *want*   4 'm having
   2 know   5 never buy
   3 'm spending 6 see

6 1 a *A*, b *N*   4 a N, b A
   2 a A, b N   5 a A, b N
   3 a N, b A

7 Line 2: are understanding → *understand*
   Line 5: aren't needing → don't need
   Line 8: You're wanting → You want
   Line 13–14: you're knowing → you know
   Line 18: are seeming → seem

1.3 Vocabulary development page 8

Vocabulary noun suffixes

1 1 *ability*, security
   2 communication, information
   3 achievement, government
   4 friendship, membership

2 1 *government*
   2 security
   3 information
   4 ability
   5 friendship

3 1 *information*
   2 improvements
   3 ability/abilities
   4 development
   5 imagination/imaginations
   6 relationships
   7 friendships

4a 1 *Ooo*   5 ●●●
    2 *Oo*   6 ●●●●
    3 ●●●   7 ●●
    4 ●●●●

Vocabulary review

5a 1 *out*   6 help
    2 touch   7 keep
    3 on   8 make
    4 in   9 up
    5 have

5b 1 bargains
    2 deals
    3 half-price
    4 special offers
    5 two for the price of one
    6 discounts
    7 items
    8 purchases
    9 shopping
    10 shoppers
    11 customers
    12 consumers

1.4 Speaking and writing page 9

Speaking asking for and giving opinions

1a 1 *P* 2 N 3 N 4 P 5 P

1b a *feel*   e think
    b some   f convinced
    c personally   g definitely
    d me   h far

2 1 *As* far as I'm concerned, …
   2 I *definitely think* that …
   3 *What* do you think about …? OR How do you *feel* about …?
   4 According *to* my wife, …!
   5 *I* really feel that …

3 1 *how*   6 don't
   2 about   7 think
   3 you   8 am / 'm
   4 me   9 far
   5 to   10 concerned

98

4a 1 As far as I'm concerned …
2 Some people say that …
3 I really feel that …
4 If you ask me, …
5 How do you feel about …?
6 Don't you think …?

Writing social media

5a 1 *c u at bday party*
2 sorry, have 2 b in London Sat
3 1 hour late 4 work cos of traffic
4 just realized some ppl r so rude n selfish

5b 1 *c u at bday party*
2 just realized some ppl r so rude n selfish
c 1 hour late 4 work cos of traffic
d sorry, have 2 b in London Sat

Unit 2 What a story!

2.1 I'll never forget that day page 10

Vocabulary describing past experiences

1a 1 *recognize*   5 remember
2 believe   6 remind
3 realized   7 wonder
4 expect

1b 1 a safari guide? *1*, 4, 7
2 a firefighter? 3, 5
3 a window cleaner? 2, 6

2a a *recognize*   e believe
b remember   f realize
c expecting   g wonder
d reminded

2b 1 *e* 2 *g* 3 *d* 4 *a* 5 *c* 6 *b* 7 *f*

Grammar narrative forms

3a **past continuous:** *was walking*, were fighting, was carrying, was talking
past simple: *thought*, ran, shot, hit, realized, noticed, wasn't hurt, destroyed, left

3b a *4* b 3 c 5 d 1 e 2

4 1 *had always dreamt*
2 had taken
3 missed
4 were waiting
5 disappeared
6 had taken
7 were going
8 hadn't seen
9 rained
10 had already gone
11 were watching

5a 1 When I got home, my wife <u>had</u> cooked my favourite dish.

2 In my childhood, I had a dog called Spot.
3 At the end of the day, he <u>was</u> exhausted.
4 Thanks, I <u>was</u> looking all over the place for that!
5 Actually, we have enough time to get there.
6 They <u>were</u> good friends at school.

5b a *1* and 4
b 2 and 5
c 3 and 6

2.2 Unbelievable? page 12

Grammar sequencing events

1a 2 / 10 / 8 / 3 / 1 / 5 / 4 / 7 / 9 / 6

2 1 *during*   4 while
2 until   5 Meanwhile
3 As soon as   6 By the time

3 1 A seven-year-old boy disappeared *while* he was playing in the garden.
2 His mother called the police as soon *as* she noticed he wasn't there.
3 *By* the time the police arrived, the neighbours had already started looking for him.
4 Several groups searched the area. *Meanwhile* OR *In the meanwhile*, a police officer interviewed the parents to identify possible suspects.
5 Everybody believed he had been kidnapped until ~~that~~ the family dog found him.
6 He had been hiding in a tree in the garden *during* the whole search. He said it was an April Fools' Day joke!

4 1 On 25 June 1947, a pilot saw several objects *while* he was flying over Washington.
2 Meanwhile, a farmer in New Mexico claimed he had found part of a flying disk.
3 He contacted the sheriff and kept the object until the Armed Forces took it away.
4 Journalists from all over America flew to the area as soon as a local newspaper printed the story.
5 Stories about aliens had already spread by the time the Air Force declared that the object wasn't a UFO, but only a weather balloon.

6 More mysterious evidence and reports came up during the following years.

Vocabulary communication

5a 1 *announced*   a told
2 interviewed   b keep
3 claimed   c admitted
4 reported   d mentioned
5 invented   e informed

5b 1 *c* 2 a 3 e 4 d 5 b

6 1 *claimed*, interviewed, admitted
2 announced, reported
3 told, kept quiet

7 1 *A famous palaeontologist claimed he had made a revolutionary discovery.*
2 Journalists from all over the world wanted to interview him.
3 The National Science Association announced he was going to be investigated for fraud.
4 He kept quiet during the investigation.
5 The scientist admitted that he had invented some information to prove his theory.
6 A national scientific magazine reported the whole story in a special edition.

8a 1 admitted /ɪd/
2 interviewed /d/
3 announced /t/
4 invented /ɪd/
5 claimed /d/
6 mentioned /d/
7 informed /d/
8 reported /ɪd/

2.3 Vocabulary development page 14

Vocabulary comment adverbs

1 1 *surprisingly*
2 Curiously
3 Remarkably
4 Fortunately
5 Naturally
6 interestingly

2b 1 The accident was serious, but luckily, no one was hurt.
2 Unfortunately, there's nothing I can do about it.
3 I got the recipe wrong, but surprisingly, everybody loved the dish.

4 Amazingly , the magician reappeared at the back of the theatre.

5 They invested a lot in marketing but, interestingly, sales continued falling.

3 1 *Fortunately* 5 Personally
   2 Luckily   6 sadly
   3 surprisingly 7 remarkably
   4 Naturally

Vocabulary review

4 Verbs for narrative: *believe*, expect, realize, recognize, remember, remind, wonder
   Verbs for communication: *admit*, announce, claim, inform, interview, invent, keep quiet, mention, tell, report

2.4 Speaking and Writing page 15

Speaking showing interest

1 1 Saving a baby – twice!
   2 A book very far from home

2a 1 *heard*   5 Someone
    2 Really   6 That
    3 believe   7 mean
    4 amazing   8 way

3a 1 N 2 I 3 N 4 I 5 I 6 N

Writing a narrative

4 1 *ago*
   2 while
   3 straightaway
   4 instant
   5 just
   6 soon
   7 end

2.5 Reading for pleasure page 16

Kidnapped

1 3 a historical adventure story

Review: Units 1 and 2 page 17

Grammar

1 1 *started*
   2 have grown
   3 was having
   4 had borrowed
   5 spend
   6 is constantly developing

2 1 *prefer*   6 as soon as
   2 *by the time* 7 during
   3 own   8 hate

4 until   **9** agree
5 want   **10** Meanwhile

Vocabulary

3 1 *gets*   5 admitted
   2 common   6 expect
   3 meet   7 believes
   4 out   8 told

Speaking

4 1 *How*   4 feel
   2 ask   5 to
   3 think

Unit 3 Life skills

3.1 Challenges page 18

Vocabulary challenges and success

1 1 *in*   5 for
   2 about   6 making
   3 make   7 be
   4 with   8 rise

2a 1 *resist*   4 avoid
    2 manage   5 observe
    3 succeed   6 achieve

3 1 *give in*
   2 rise to
   3 thinking about
   4 managed to
   5 succeeding in
   6 wait for
   7 prefer to

Grammar ability

4 1 a 2 b 3 c 4 c 5 c 6 a

5 1 *I'm afraid we can't return the documents you sent.*
   2 Did they manage to find their way back easily?
   3 Tina wasn't able to get a holiday job last summer.
   4 Some students succeeded in passing all the exams.
   5 Can you lift such heavy bags?
   6 Are you sure that Jack will be able to find the hotel?
   7 Lars didn't manage to pass his driving test.
   8 Do you think Anna can come on Sunday?

6 1 *didn't succeed in getting*
   2 couldn't play; wasn't able to play
   3 will be able to buy
   4 managed to sell/succeeded in selling
   5 can't act
   6 can't sing
   7 could dance/was able to dance
   8 could cook/was able to cook

3.2 Faking it? page 20

Vocabulary work skills

1 1 c 2 d 3 a 4 b 5 f 6 e

2 1 *work hard*
   2 setting goals
   3 take responsibility
   4 making decisions
   5 solving problems
   6 managed teams

3 1 managing 4 tasking
   2 working   5 persuading
   3 being   6 being

4 a 6 b 3 c 5 d 1 e 4 f 2

Grammar obligation, permission and possibility

5 1 *has to*   6 don't have to
   2 can   7 can
   3 can't   8 had to
   4 have to   9 didn't have to
   5 mustn't   10 had to

6a 1 You <u>have</u> to wear a shirt and tie.
    2 You <u>mustn't</u> wear jeans.
    3 You <u>needn't</u> start work at nine.
    4 You can <u>start</u> at any time.
    The modal is stressed in 1, 2 and 3.

7 1 *We can dress down on Fridays.*
   2 You don't have to wear a tie.
   3 A few years ago, employees couldn't check personal emails at work.
   4 You can't eat sandwiches at your work station.
   5 In the past, employees had to sign out every time they left the building.
   6 You need to book holidays six months in advance.
   7 You must switch off your mobile phone at work.
   8 From the start of next month, we are able to start work between 8 and 10 a.m.

3.3 Vocabulary development page 22

Vocabulary compound adjectives

1a 1 well-*known*
    2 left-handed
    3 short-sleeved
    4 good-looking
    5 English-speaking
    6 home-made

1b a 2 b 3 c 4 d 5 e 1 f 6

2 1 *fifty-minute* 5 over-priced
2 full-time 6 easy-going
3 second-hand 7 hard-working
4 five-star 8 500-page

Vocabulary review

3 1 *c* 2 f 3 a 4 e 5 h 6 g
7 b 8 d

4 1 *working* 5 managing
2 taking 6 being
3 tasking 7 making
4 setting 8 solving

3.4 Speaking and writing page 23

Speaking practical instructions

1a 1 ✓ 5 ✓
2 ✓ 6
3 ✓ 7
4 ✓ 8 ✓

1b 1 *make* 5 like
2 show 6 done
3 thing 7 doing
4 show 8 next

Writing writing an opinion paragraph

2a c doing

2b 1 *for instance*
2 such as
3 too
4 also
5 for example
6 On top of that

Unit 4 Space

4.1 Living on water page 24

Vocabulary living on water

1 1 b 2 b 3 a 4 b 5 a 6 b

2 1 c 2 a 3 e 4 b 5 d

3 1 *ferry* 6 floats
2 sea 7 beaches
3 coast 8 waves
4 island 9 inland
5 mainland 10 canals

Grammar *will/be going to* for predictions and decisions

4 1 *isn't going to*
2 won't
3 're going to
4 'll
5 're going to

5a 1 *'m going to* 5 will
2 're going to 6 will
3 're going to 7 'll
4 'll

6 1 *'re going to stay*
2 'll go
3 're going to climb
4 're going to book
5 will destroy
6 'll tell

4.2 Forest bathing page 26

Vocabulary the natural world

1 1 *b* 2 c 3 f 4 d 5 a 6 e

2 1 *fresh air* 4 landscape
2 season 5 sunset
3 sunshine 6 scenery

3 1 *landscape* 4 sunset
2 season 5 sunshine
3 fresh air 6 scenery

4 1 *landscape* 4 cliffs
2 valleys 5 soil
3 waterfalls 6 scenery

Grammar probability

5 1 *b* 2 c 3 c 4 b 5 b

6a 1 *will definitely join*
2 are likely to plant
3 will definitely not survive/ definitely won't survive
4 will possibly take part
5 probably won't need
6 is unlikely to succeed

7 1 *won't* 4 might
2 will 5 likely
3 may 6 will probably

4.3 Vocabulary development page 28

Vocabulary idiomatic phrases about places

1 1 *at* 5 for
2 anywhere 6 back
3 sardines 7 down
4 of 8 over

2 1 *are making themselves at home*
2 run out of space
3 get rid of
4 all over the place
5 settling down
6 feel at home

Vocabulary review

3 1 *peak* 5 canal
2 coast 6 forest
3 ferry 7 season
4 lake 8 island

4 1 *b, c* 4 c
2 a, c 5 b, c
3 b, c 6 b, c

4.4 Speaking and writing page 29

Speaking enquiries

1a a 3 b 4 c 1 d 2

1b **Conversation 1**
Thanks for your help, I really appreciate it. I'm size 44, by the way.
Conversation 2
Could you tell me when the 68 leaves?
Conversation 3
I wonder if you could help me transfer £30,000 to my new account?
Conversation 4
Just one last question. It cost me £80 last time.

2a 1 *can I*
2 wonder if
3 aware that
4 Could you
5 with anything
6 you tell
7 I appreciate

Writing avoiding repetition

3a Mo: 8 town: 4 old: 2 good: 2

3b 1 *centre* 5 hometown
2 it 6 place
3 fascinating 7 there
4 traditional 8 great

4.5 Listening for pleasure page 30

Architect Shigeru Ban

1 1 *Cardboard* 5 shelters
2 architect 6 paper tubing
3 architecture 7 refugees
4 recycled 8 designs

3 1 known 5 homes
2 disaster 6 wood
3 solution 7 easy
4 refugee 8 saved

Review: Units 3 and 4 page 31

Grammar

1 1 *Andy wasn't able to open the front door.*
2 We definitely won't get home before nine o'clock.
3 I didn't manage to finish the exercise.
4 You don't have to stay here all evening.
5 They are unlikely to get much better at maths.
6 What does she need to do to pass the exam?

2
1 can't 4 couldn't
2 I'm going to 5 will
3 might 6 don't have to

3
1 *will* 5 may
2 can 6 will
3 couldn't 7 won't
4 can't

Vocabulary

4
1 *working under pressure*
2 rise to the challenge
3 take responsibility
4 deal with problems
5 succeed in achieving

Speaking

5
D How do you make a really good paper aeroplane?
T It's really easy. Let me show you.
D Thanks, Tracy. Here, I've got some paper.
T Right, the first thing you do is fold the piece of paper in half.
D OK, what next?
T Well, then you fold over these ends. You do it like this. Make sure they're straight.
D Straight? How do you do that, exactly? Can you show me again?
T Sure. Look. After doing this, you just fold the wings back, and there you are, a perfect aeroplane.

Unit 5 Entertainment

5.1 Universally popular? page 32

Vocabulary going to the movies

1
1 *scene*, performance
2 plays, characters
3 stars, set
4 plot, cast

2
1 c 2 e 3 f 4 b 5 a 6 d

3
1 plot 5 performance
2 set 6 cast
3 stars 7 special effects
4 character

Grammar -*ing* form and infinitive with *to*

4
1 1b Do you feel like going out later?
2a Would you like to go out this evening?
2 1a Oscar can't afford to go to a gym.
2b Anja can't stand going to nightclubs.
3 1b On Friday, we recommend having dinner at Pierre's bistro.
2a On Sunday, we hope to eat out at Luigi's pizzeria.

4 1a Sally agreed to join the science club.
2b Luisa thought about joining the army.
5 1b Paul enjoys doing dance classes.
2a Yves plans to go to jazz concerts.

5
1 Thank You for *Smoking*
2 We Need to Talk About Kevin
3 How to Succeed in Business without Really Trying
4 Stop the World: I Want to Get Off
5 Dr Strangelove, or How I Learned to Stop Worrying and Love the Bomb
6 Can't Stand Losing You!

6
1 *watching* 6 falling
2 taking 7 living
3 to promote 8 to give
4 to see 9 to be
5 to find 10 to be

5.2 Mosquito smasher! page 34

Vocabulary adjectives to describe a video game

1
Positive: *surprising*, intelligent, entertaining, amusing, original, enjoyable
Negative: *ordinary*, silly, dull, violent, unexciting, predictable, disappointing

2
1 *entertaining* 4 original
2 intelligent 5 enjoyable
3 surprising 6 amusing

3
1 *dull* 4 predictable
2 disappointing 5 violent
3 ordinary 6 silly

4a
1 *b* 2 d 3 a 4 c

Grammar present perfect simple and past simple

5
1 *ever* 5 since
2 just 6 already
3 ago 7 never
4 last 8 for

6
1 *'ve made* 4 've changed
2 haven't started 5 've worked
3 wasn't 6 watched

7
1 *have made* 5 have gone
2 filmed 6 have needed
3 has been 7 starred
4 has become 8 have visited

5.3 Vocabulary development page 36

Vocabulary extreme adjectives

1a
1 *exhausted* 5 terrifying
2 delicious 6 brilliant
3 freezing 7 terrible
4 enormous 8 astonishing

2
1 *tired* 5 astonishing
2 impossible 6 tasty
3 cold 7 clever
4 scary 8 brilliant

Vocabulary review

3
1 *plot* 5 cast
6 characters 7 remake
2 set 8 scenes
3 star 9 effects
4 performance

4
1 a 2 b 3 c 4 b

5.4 Speaking and writing page 37

Speaking comparing and recommending

1a
1 The Shawshank Redemption
2 The Godfather
3 Jaws
4 Raiders of the Lost Ark
5 Star Wars

1b
A	B
1 *c*	1 c
2 d	2 d
3 a	3 a
4 b	4 b

2a 1 *b* 2 c 3 a

Writing a film review

3
1 cast: 2
2 plot: 1, 2, 3
3 setting: 1
4 special effects: 1, 3

4
1 *Despite* 4 Although
2 in spite of 5 However
3 however 6 even though

Unit 6 In control?

6.1 Man and machine page 38

Vocabulary machines

1
1 *park* 5 wheel
2 lane 6 injured
3 accident 7 at
4 limit 8 lights

2a
1 motorway
2 injured
3 accident
4 overtake
5 driverless

3a 1 B 2 C 3 A

3b 1 *injured*   7 lights
2 accident   8 park
3 motorway   9 lane
4 jam   10 overtake
5 busy   11 junction
6 wheel   12 brake

Grammar defining and non-defining relative clauses

4 1 *b, c* 2 b 3 a,c 4 b
5 a,b 6 a

5 1 a *who* b which/that
2 a – b which c which/that
3 a which b which
4 a – b who
5 a which/that b which c –

6 1 *Össur is a global company that manufactures prosthetic limbs.*
2 The company's engineers, whose designs have won awards, have developed many artificial knees.
3 American medical engineer Van Phillips, who designed a carbon fibre prosthetic foot, sold his famous product to Össur.
4 Össur sponsors Paralympian athletes, which is something they are proud of.
5 The Power Knee is just one product they manufacture.
6 During the presentation, which was held at Össur's headquarters, we heard about the latest developments in prosthetics.

6.2 Controlling the weather? page 40

Vocabulary climate and extreme weather

1 1 *c* 2 b 3 d 4 f 5 a 6 e
Crop damage, destroyed housing and water shortages describe the effects of extreme weather events.

2 1 *crop damage*
2 global warming
3 climate change
4 water shortages
5 high temperatures
6 destroyed housing

3 1 *heatwave*   5 winds
2 drought   6 storm
3 rainfall   7 fires
4 floods   8 landslide

Grammar present perfect simple and continuous

4 1 *I've been waiting here for ages.*
2 Have you seen the film yet?
3 Sally hasn't been living there long.
4 They've already had lunch.
5 Has it stopped raining yet?
6 How long have you been sitting there?

5a 1 *a* 2 b 3 a 4 b 5 a 6 a

6 1 *have/'ve been using*
2 have helped, have been helping
3 have left
4 has been using
5 have become
6 have developed
7 have been
8 has saved

6.3 Vocabulary development page 42

Vocabulary adjective suffixes

1 1 *a* 2 b 3 c 4 b 5 c 6 a

2 1 *nervous*   4 healthy
2 reliable   5 careless
3 colourful   6 personal

3 1 *nervous*   6 acceptable
2 stressful   7 personal
3 typical   8 social
4 cheerful   9 traditional
5 funny   10 dusty

4a 1 *social*, careless, lucky
2 acceptable, enjoyable
3 typical, practical, sociable

Vocabulary review

6 1 *at*   6 wheel
2 lane   7 limit
3 junction   8 lights
4 jam   9 accident
5 driverless 10 injured

7 1 a 2 a 3 b 4 b 5 a 6 a

6.4 Speaking and writing page 43

Speaking changing arrangements

1a 1 b 2 b 3 c

1b 1 e 2 d 3 b 4 c 5 a 6 g 7 f
Phrases in the conversations ✓: 1, 2, 3, 6, c, f

1c b I'm available then.
4 I'll confirm it with you.
e I'm not available then.
7 Our arrangements have changed, I'm afraid.

Writing a professional email

2a From a student: 2
From a member of staff: 1

2b 1 help   5 apologize
2 wasn't able 6 Unfortunately
3 like   7 wonder
4 Many   8 wishes

6.5 Reading for pleasure page 44

The Everest Story

1 rope, ice axe, backpack, climbing boots, oxygen masks, tent, goggles, etc.

Review: Units 5 and 6 page 45

Grammar

1 1 *driving*   5 to buy
2 taking   6 taking
3 which   7 which
4 whose   8 that

2 1 *began*
2 has been
3 only showed
4 has also shown
5 have become
6 saw
7 loved
8 has been making

Vocabulary

3 1 *fall*   5 wave
2 wheel   6 effects
3 change   7 hero
4 jam   8 limit

4 1 *accident*   4 shortages
2 junction   5 damage
3 injured   6 temperatures

5 1 very predictable
2 absolutely terrifying
3 absolutely freezing
4 very stressful
5 very nervous
6 really surprising

Speaking

6 1 *I wouldn't recommend going to see it.*
2 It's much funnier than I thought it would be.
3 It's nothing like as good as his first film.
4 I can't make the party on Saturday.
5 I'm meant to be babysitting then.
6 I'm afraid I've got something else on.
7 I'll confirm it with you later.

Unit 7 Ambitions

7.1 Good prospects page 46

Vocabulary working conditions

1 1 c 2 f 3 d 4 a 5 b 6 e

2 1 *career prospects*
2 be made redundant
3 rent-free accommodation
4 holiday pay
5 working hours
6 job satisfaction

3 1 *unemployed*
2 redundant
3 working
4 occupation
5 working conditions
6 salary

4 1 *qualifications*
2 rent-free accommodation
3 promotion
4 career prospects
5 job satisfaction
6 sick pay
Answers 2, 3 and 6 won't help you get the job.

Grammar *used to* and *would*

5 1 *used to feel*
2 didn't use to like
3 correct
4 went
5 correct
6 used to work
7 used to be responsible

6a 1 *I used to spend more than two hours on the bus every day.*
2 I didn't use to see much of my children during the week.
3 People used to interrupt me all the time.
4 ✗
5 I used to hate wearing a tie every day.
6 I used to feel depressed on Sundays, thinking about going to the office the next day.

6b 1 I would spend more than an hour on the bus every day.
2 I wouldn't see much of my children during the week.
3 People would interrupt me all the time.
6 I would feel depressed on Sundays, thinking about going to the office the next day.

7b 1 *I used to work at home.*
2 I'd go by car every day. I never walked.

3 I used a copy from the Web.
4 I'd travel abroad a lot.

7.2 Ask an expert page 48

Vocabulary high achievers

1 1 *determined to*
2 a hard-working
3 achievement
4 An expert
5 A champion
6 ambitious

2 1 *achieved*   4 fame
2 famous   5 talented
3 awards   6 well-known

3 1 *experts*   5 well known
2 achieved   6 talented
3 determined   7 achievement
4 hard-working   8 champions

Grammar question forms

4a 1 How many self-help books *have* you read?
2 Who **told** you about *The Art of Doing*?
3 **Do** you remember where you bought it?
4 Can I ask which your favourite chapter **was**?
5 What **changed** in your life after reading this book?
6 Who **would** you recommend this book to?

4b Object questions: 1 and 6
Subject questions: 2 and 5
Indirect questions: 3 and 4

5a a 5 b 3 c 4 d 2 e 6 f 1

6 1 *Can I ask you what your name is?*
2 which famous person you admire
3 if you consider yourself successful
4 who the most talented person in your family is
5 if she's ever received an award

7 1 a *received a Nobel prize*
  b *did Englert and Higgs receive*
2 a received the United Nations Human Rights Award
  b did Malala Yousafzai receive
3 a has sold over 150 million books
  b books has Paulo Coelho
4 a won three gold medals
  b did Usain Bolt win
5 a became a billionaire
  b did Liu Qiangdong become

7.3 Vocabulary development page 50

Vocabulary collocations

1 1 e 2 d 3 g 4 f 5 h 6 a
7 c 8 b

2 1 *completely different,* came up with the idea
2 make progress, temporary jobs
3 take risks, got promoted
4 think creatively, did his best

3 1 *job*   7 satisfaction
2 best   8 following
3 get   9 take
4 hugely   10 supervise
5 completely   11 higher
6 obey

Vocabulary review

4 **Working conditions**
career prospects
holiday pay
job satisfaction
make someone redundant
promotion
qualifications
occupation
rent-free accommodation
salary
sick pay
unemployed
working hours

High achievers
achieve fame
achievements
ambitious
awards
champion
determined
expert
famous
hard-working
talented
well-known

7.4 Speaking and writing page 51

Speaking clarification

1 1 a different job
2 problems with journalists recently
3 took the job

2a 1 c 2 a 3 d 4 b

2b Ask for clarification: 1, 2
Get time to think: 4
Give clarification: 3

3a 1 what   4 give
2 mean   5 let
3 sure

3b Meeting: Conversation 2
Press conference: Conversation 1

Writing an application letter or email

4 1 *main*
2 attached
3 would
4 opportunity
5 forward
6 further
7 regarding

5 a 7 b 2 c 1 d 4 e 3 f 6 g 5

Unit 8 Choices

8.1 World happiness report page 52

Vocabulary happiness factors

1 1 *cultural activities*
2 leisure time
3 balanced diet
4 high taxes
5 healthcare
6 strong economy
7 physical activity

2a 1 *childcare* 4 poverty
2 neighbour 5 volunteer
3 pollution

2c happy: 1, 2 and 5
unhappy: 2, 3, 4

3 1 *healthcare* 5 physical
2 economy 6 activities
3 pollution 7 leisure
4 neighbours 8 volunteer

Grammar real conditionals

4 1 *can learn* 5 meditate
2 feel 6 start
3 won't be 7 can be
4 can get rid 8 look

5a In conditional sentences, the intonation usually rises in the *first* part and falls in the *second*.

5b a 1 b 2 c 1 d 1 e 2 f 1

8.2 What makes a hero? page 54

Vocabulary personality and behaviour

1 a *educated and kind*
b brave and heroic
c honest and responsible
d lucky and generous
e calm and responsible
f kind and generous

2 1 *selfish* 4 afraid
2 embarrassed 5 calm
3 ordinary 6 crazy

3 1 *embarrassed* 6 brave
2 heroic 7 honest
3 calm 8 crazy
4 afraid 9 educated
5 ordinary

Grammar unreal conditionals

4 1 *saw* 5 Would
2 would 6 gave
3 got 7 was
4 would 8 would

5a 1 *'d definitely tell*
2 'd confess
3 'd never do
4 gave
5 'd jump
6 had
7 would you do
8 wouldn't risk
9 was
10 'd try
11 didn't have

6 1 If a disabled person *needed* to cross a street, I would help them.
2 I would stop my car if someone needed help on a highway at night. (no comma)
3 I might give blood *if* the local hospital needed it.
4 I *would carry* an elderly woman's shopping to her house, even if it wasn't near mine.
5 I would call an ambulance if I saw a cyclist hit by a car. (no 'if' at beginning)
6 I would help strangers if I *could*, but I'm usually in a hurry.

7 1 *if I were younger*
2 I were you, I'd
3 would help if I knew
4 would be generous if we
5 might do something if
6 if there were more

8.3 Vocabulary development page 56

Vocabulary prefixes

1 *mis-*: misbehave, misjudge, misunderstand
re-: reappear, renew
in-: inconvenient, informal
over-: overeat, overspend

2 1 *renew* 6 misunderstand
2 overeat 7 informal
3 misbehaving 8 misjudged
4 inconvenient 9 overspend
5 reappeared

3 1 Inactive 4 incorrect
2 rearrange 5 misspelled
3 overreacting 6 rescheduled

4 1 *misunderstood*
2 rearrange/reschedule
3 misbehaving
4 replace
5 overspent

Vocabulary review

5 1 *balanced diet*
2 physical activity
3 healthcare
4 pollution
5 generous
6 kind
7 afraid
8 selfish

8.4 Speaking and writing page 57

Speaking giving a talk

1 1 D 2 A 3 C 4 B

2a Introduction: *A* and C
Main body: D
Conclusion: B

2b 1 *Firstly* 5 finish
2 Then 6 talk
3 finally 7 on
4 looked 8 last

Writing taking notes

3 1 d 2 f 3 a 4 b 5 e 6 g
7 i 8 h 9 c

4 1 *distr* 6 ppl
2 foc 7 curts
3 urgt 8 mob
4 conn 9 prof
5 h/day

8.5 Listening for pleasure page 58

Eating for free

1 1 b collecting seaweed
2 c foraging for mushrooms
3 f taking waste food from a supermarket
4 d growing your own produce
5 e picking berries
6 a bartering for food with friends

3 1 buying 5 collecting
2 spent 6 would save
3 growing 7 waste
4 foraged 8 bartered

Grammar

1 1 *are*   6 to
   2 will/might   7 if
   3 feel/be   8 use
   4 unless   9 used
   5 would

Vocabulary

2 1 *healthcare*   5 salary
   2 satisfaction   6 leisure
   3 working   7 holiday
   4 childcare   8 economy

3 1 *well-known*   6 ordinary
   2 expert   7 heroic
   3 brave   8 responsible
   4 determined   9 generous
   5 award   10 afraid

Speaking

4a 1 Let's move *on* now to talk about the
     effects of social media.
   2 I'm *here* to talk to you about
     decisions.
   3 Could you give *me* some examples
     of your achievements?
   4 So we've looked *at* the main
     factors that create stress.
   5 What I *mean* is that I have good
     time management skills.
   6 Well, *for* instance, I designed my
     last company's social networking
     page.

4b talk: 1, 2 and 4
   job interview: 3, 5 and 6

Unit 9 Appearances

9.1 Real beauty? page 60

Vocabulary describing physical
appearance

1 1 *face*   5 stubble
   2 jaw   6 moustache
   3 forehead   7 bald
   4 curly

2 1 *c* 2 d 3 a 4 e 5 b

3 1 *long*
   2 slim, in her twenties
   3 round, double, good
   4 large, thick
   5 elderly, overweight

Grammar comparison

4 1 *more*   5 less
   2 than   6 as
   3 isn't   7 bit
   4 much   8 most

5 1 *slimmer*
   2 most attractive
   3 more interested
   4 curlier
   5 thinner
   6 vainest

6 1 *Maria was a lot less supportive*
     than I thought she would be.
   2 Luke is the most insecure person I
     know.
   3 Mohsen is far more confident than
     his brother, Kamal.
   4 My hair used to be much shorter
     than it is now.
   5 This is the most valuable painting
     in the museum.

7 1 *much older*
   2 as young as
   3 far less worried than
   4 even more surprised than
   5 as wide as
   6 no more unusual than
   7 a lot better
   8 as vain as
   9 as fast as
  10 the most exciting

9.2 Paintings page 62

Vocabulary describing paintings

1 1 *soft*   5 traditional
   2 warm   6 seems
   3 modern   7 tells a story
   4 old-fashioned   8 curves

2 1 *historical*   4 old-fashioned
   2 colourful   5 curves
   3 tells a story   6 mysterious

3a 1 historical   5 modern
   2 colourful   6 traditional
   3 detailed   7 old-fashioned
   4 mysterious

4 1 the middle of
   2 the foreground
   3 the bottom right-hand corner
   4 the left
   5 front of
   6 the background

Grammar deduction and speculation

5a 1 *must*   5 might
   2 can't   6 can't
   3 could   7 must
   4 could   8 must

6 1 *must*   6 might
   2 might   7 must
   3 might   8 can't
   4 might   9 might
   5 can't   10 must

9.3 Vocabulary development
page 64

Vocabulary phrasal verbs

1 1 ✓
   2 *looking after them*
   3 taken off
   4 ✓
   5 thought about your choices
   6 make him out
   7 broken down
   8 ✓

2a 1 *round*   5 on
   2 up   6 up
   3 off   7 up
   4 after   8 across

Vocabulary review

3 1 *f* 2 b 3 j 4 e 5 c 6 a
   7 d 8 g 9 h 10 i

4 1 *b* 2 a 3 a 4 a 5 b 6 a

9.4 Speaking and writing page 65

Speaking making complaints

1a 2 and 4

1b 1 something
   2 about
   3 What's
   4 know, sounds
   5 problem, on
   6 What, about
   7 could
   8 sure, down
   9 Do, something

2a 1 Do you <u>think</u> you could turn your
     music <u>down</u>?
   2 Your dog's <u>barking</u> <u>keeps</u> <u>waking</u>
     me <u>up</u>.
   3 Sorry to <u>bother</u> you, but your
     <u>rubbish</u> bin is in front of our
     <u>house</u>.
   4 The <u>problem's</u> been going on for
     <u>months</u>!
   5 I'm <u>sorry</u> about <u>that</u>. I'll make sure
     it's <u>quiet</u> <u>tomorrow</u>.

Writing taking part in online
discussions

3a 1 c 2 b 3 a

3b 1 *That's a great question*
   2 Thanks for posting it
   3 Thanks for commenting on my
     post
   4 As you say
   5 You make some good points

Unit 10 Compete and cooperate

10.1 Crowd-funding page 66

Vocabulary business

1
1 cash
2 a loan
3 a risk
4 a guarantee
5 an investor
6 funding
7 a profit

2
1 in   4 out
2 in   5 of
3 up

3
1 set up a business
2 give a guarantee
3 raise a million
4 meet an investor
5 short of cash

4
1 set   6 make
2 take   7 found
3 present   8 became
4 get   9 backed
5 increased   10 sharing

Grammar passives

5
1 is prepared
2 began
3 have been found
4 were being farmed
5 started
6 was made

6
1 was invented
2 was sold
3 is made
4 has been manufactured
5 is used
6 were introduced

7
1 started
2 was set
3 is made
4 contains
5 can be bought
6 are prepared
7 are made
8 is prepared
9 find
10 are (being) sold

10.2 Competitive sport page 68

Vocabulary competitive sport

1
1 final   4 winner
2 competitive   5 against
3 tournaments   6 race

2
1 competed   4 taken
2 played   5 lost
3 won   6 broke

3
1 competitive   4 race
2 tournament   5 final
3 team

Grammar using articles: *a/an*, *the*, – (no article)

4
1 a   2 –   3 a   4 –   5 –   6 –
7 the   8 –   9 the   10 –
11 the   12 –

5a
In 1, 2 and 3, *a*, *an* and *the* are pronounced with a weak /ə/ sound, but in 4 *the* is pronounced /ðɪː/ because it is followed by a vowel sound.

6
1 –   2 the   3 the   4 a   5 the
6 the   7 a   8 a   9 the   10 –
11 a   12 the

10.3 Vocabulary development page 70

Vocabulary phrases with *take* and *have*

1
1 take   4 take
2 has   5 had
3 took   6 take

2a
1 have   4 take
2 take   5 have
3 don't have

2b a 3   b 1   c 4   d 5   e 2

3
1 a   2 a   3 b   4 a   5 b   6 a   7 b
8 b   9 a   10 b   11 b   12 a

4
1 d   2 e   3 a   4 b   5 f   6 c

10.4 Speaking and writing page 71

Speaking making recommendations

1
1 ✓ American football and basketball

2a 1 e   2 c   3 f   4 a   5 d   6 b

Writing changes and differences

3a 1 T   2 F

3b
1 compared   5 contrast
2 Whereas   6 Whilst before
3 now it is   7 now
4 changes

10.5 Reading for pleasure page 72

Nelson Mandela

1 1 f   2 e   3 b   4 a   5 c   6 d

Review: Units 9 and 10 page 73

Grammar

1
1 could   2 a   3 the   4 less
5 must

2
1 much more difficult
2 as popular as
3 far easier than
4 the most talented

3
1 was invented
2 was picked
3 have been played
4 is named
5 weren't written
6 wasn't formed
7 was held
8 have been given

Vocabulary

4
1 a aged   b built   c shape
2 a spiky   b large   c stubble
3 a team   b tournament
   c final
4 a detailed   b bright   c stories
5 a bottom   b mysterious
   c seems

Speaking

5 1 c   2 d   3 b   4 a   5 e

Unit 11 Consequences

11.1 Outlaws page 74

Vocabulary crime

1 1 b   2 c   3 b   4 a

2
1 burglary   4 robbers
2 stolen   5 theft
3 captured   6 stealing

3a 1 /t/   2 /d/   3 /ɪd/   4 /t/   5 /ɪd/

4
1 steal   5 suspected
2 arrested   6 burglar
3 sentenced   7 stolen
4 theft

Grammar unreal past conditional

5
1 hadn't been, wouldn't have
2 hadn't spent, would probably have
3 might never, hadn't left
4 hadn't shot, have become
5 not have died, had made

7
1 probably wouldn't have been
2 hadn't been
3 had found
4 probably wouldn't have committed / would probably not have committed
5 hadn't told

6 probably wouldn't have gone /
  would probably not have gone
7 hadn't spent
8 probably wouldn't have known /
  would probably not have known
9 hadn't started
10 might have escaped

11.2 I should never have clicked 'send'! page 76

Vocabulary behaviour on social media

1 1 *regrets*   4 say
   2 insulted   5 upset
   3 feel

2 1 *rude*   5 regret
   2 nasty   6 upset
   3 passionate   7 tweets
   4 unpleasant   8 difference

3a 1 *insult*
   2 unpleasant
   3 regret
   4 upset

4 1 *made*   6 careless
   2 replaced   7 upset
   3 say   8 stand
   4 speak   9 nasty
   5 feel   10 victim

Grammar *should/shouldn't have*

5a 1 *She should have spoken up.*
   2 They shouldn't have criticized other
     celebrities.
   3 Should he have been so critical?
   4 He shouldn't have sent that nasty
     tweet.
   5 You should have been more careful.
   6 Shouldn't you be studying for your
     exams?

6 1 He shouldn't have posted the video!
   2 She shouldn't have sent the text!
   3 She should have spoken to her
     parents!
   4 He should have joined Twitter
     sooner.
   5 She should have written in her blog
     already.
   6 He shouldn't have spent so long on
     the internet.
   7 He should have replied to my emails.
   8 Annie shouldn't have posted the
     photo of Sarah.

7 1 *have expressed*
   2 shouldn't have said
   3 should have listened
   4 shouldn't have threatened
   5 should have thought
   6 shouldn't have done

7 shouldn't have posted
8 should have realized
9 Should he have joined

11.3 Vocabulary development page 78

Vocabulary words with multiple meanings

1 1 *waved*, waves
   2 fine, fine
   3 match, matches
   4 changed, change
   5 showers, shower

2 1 *jam*   4 rock
   2 square   5 bank
   3 light   6 key

Vocabulary review

3 1 *d* 2 a 3 e 4 f 5 b 6 c

4 1 *robbery*   3 burglar
   2 theft   4 steal

5 1 *regret*
   2 criticize, rude, upset
   3 Speak, feel
   4 issues, make
   5 cyber
   6 stand
   7 face
   8 replace

11.4 Speaking and writing page 79

Speaking decisions

1a 1 *both*
   2 both
   3 Conversation 2
   4 Conversation 1
   5 Conversation 2
   6 both

1b 1 *move*   4 settled
   2 convinced   5 running
   3 admit   6 Are

1c a *1*,5 b 2,3 c 6 d 4

2a 1 *we move on*
   2 must admit that
   3 option would be
   4 settled then

2b No, they won't, because they want
   lectures to start later.

Writing apologizing

3 1 *sorry*
   2 hope
   3 forgive
   4 apologies, inconvenience
   5 understand
   6 apologize

Unit 12 Influence
12.1 Advertising page 80

Vocabulary advertising

1 1 *products*   5 slogans
   2 adverts   6 logos
   3 posters   7 brands
   4 billboards

2a 1 *amusing*   3 confusing
   2 persuasive   4 effective

3 1 *d* 2 e 3 b 4 a 5 f 6 c

4 1 *product*
   2 brand
   3 logo
   4 adverts
   5 memorable
   6 slogan
   7 clever
   8 amusing
   9 persuasive
  10 effective

Grammar reported speech

5 1 *is*
   2 haven't designed
   3 am, will
   4 won't

6 1 *advertising was the greatest art
     form of the 20th century*
   2 many a small thing had been made
     large
   3 ninety-nine per cent of advertising
     didn't sell anything
   4 advertising had done more to cause
   5 you/people/one never saw good
     poetry in advertising
   6 had left advertising as fast as he
     could

7 1 *he was a junior copywriter and was
     learning how to design ads and
     write slogans*
   2 he had started working there at WPP
     in London
   3 was one of the largest advertising
     agencies
   4 involved designing adverts for their
     clients'
   5 he was really busy
   6 he was hoping to be promoted

12.2 How to persuade and influence people page 82

Vocabulary persuading people

1 1 *saw*   4 got
   2 brought   5 convinced
   3 won   6 overcame

2a 1 *I won them over.*
2 He got his own way.
3 They brought us round to their way of thinking.
4 She saw it my way.

3 1 *persuade our friends*
2 bring them round
3 our own way
4 win us over
5 convince us to

Grammar reported questions

4 1 *b* 2 a 3 a 4 b 5 a

5 1 The interviewer *asked me how long I had worked in advertising.*
2 He wondered why I had decided to apply for that job.
3 He asked what projects I was working on at that time.
4 He asked me if I was hoping to be promoted in the next few months.
5 He asked me what I found interesting about my job.
6 He asked me if I was going to travel back to Brussels the next day.

6 1 *How long have you worked in advertising?*
2 Why have you decided to apply for this job?
3 What projects are you working on now/at the moment/at this time?
4 Are you hoping to be promoted in the next few months?
5 What do you find interesting about your job?
6 Are you going to travel back to Brussels tomorrow?

7 1 The interviewer asked me if I could tell him about an advertising campaign that hadn't worked.
2 The interviewer asked me why I thought it had failed.
3 He asked me if I had ever been in a situation where I had led a team.
4 He asked me how others had responded to my leadership.
5 He asked me if I ever had disagreements with my clients about marketing plans.
6 He asked me what I did to resolve those disagreements.

8 1 *The interviewer called and asked me when I could start.*
2 He asked me if I would sign the work contract that afternoon.
3 He asked me what hours I wanted to work.

4 He asked if/whether I was ready to start work there the following Monday.
5 He asked me how much they had paid me in my last job.
6 He asked if/whether I was prepared to work in their office abroad.

12.3 Vocabulary development
page 84

Vocabulary development dependent prepositions

1 1 in 2 at 3 to 4 in 5 for 6 for

2 1 *in*   6 of
2 about   7 to
3 in   8 for
4 about   9 to
5 on   10 on

Vocabulary review

3 1 *advert*   5 poster
2 logo   6 product
3 billboard 7 slogan
4 brand

4 1 e 2 d 3 f 4 a 5 g 6 c 7 b

5 1 *right*   4 way
2 own   5 over
3 round

12.4 Speaking and writing page 85

Speaking agreeing and disagreeing

1a **Conversation 1**
1 a   2 a
Conversation 2
1 a   2 b
Conversation 3
1 b   2 a

1b Conversation 1: b, c
Conversation 2: a, d
Conversation 3: b, d

Writing advantages and disadvantages essay

2a 2

2b a 6 b 1 c 3 d 5 e 4 f 8
g 2 h 7

12.5 Listening for pleasure page 86

Scent branding

1 1 e 2 h 3 f 4 c 5 b 6 d
7 g 8 a

2 Option b is correct.

4 1 *talked*   5 went on
2 remember 6 tell
3 told   7 gave
4 explained 8 talk

Review: Units 11 and 12 page 87

Grammar

1 1 *wanted to work in an advertising agency.*
2 had worked on a really exciting advertising campaign the year before.
3 were hoping to start a new company the following year.
4 how many employees I had in my company.
5 if we did any market research before launching a new product.
6 what I was doing the next/following day.

2 1 *should have known*
2 shouldn't have trusted
3 wanted
4 should have cancelled
5 had installed
6 should have done
7 had made
8 wouldn't be/wouldn't have been

Vocabulary

3 1 *victim*   4 robbed
2 robber   5 to
3 arrested

4 1 c 2 f 3 a 4 e 5 b 6 d

Speaking

5 1 Could we move *on* now, please?
2 You must admit this one looks much better.
3 Are there any other suggestions?
4 That's just what I was planning!
5 I agree up to a point.
6 I couldn't agree more.

Irregular verbs

Infinitive	Past simple	Past participle
be	was/were	been
beat	beat	beaten
become	became	become
begin	began	begun
bite	bit	bitten
blow	blew	blown
break	broke	broken
bring	brought	brought
build	built	built
buy	bought	bought
can	could	been able to
catch	caught	caught
choose	chose	chosen
come	came	come
cost	cost	cost
cut	cut	cut
dig	dug	dug
do	did	done
draw	drew	drawn
dream	dreamt/dreamed	dreamt/dreamed
drink	drank	drunk
drive	drove	driven
eat	ate	eaten
fall	fell	fallen
feed	fed	fed
feel	felt	felt
fight	fought	fought
find	found	found
fly	flew	flown
forget	forgot	forgotten
forgive	forgave	forgiven
freeze	froze	frozen
get	got	got
give	gave	given
go	went	gone/been
grow	grew	grown
have	had	had
hear	heard	heard
hide	hid	hidden
hit	hit	hit
hold	held	held
hurt	hurt	hurt
keep	kept	kept
know	knew	known
lay	laid	laid
lead	led	led
learn	learnt/learned	learnt/learned
leave	left	left

Infinitive	Past simple	Past participle
lend	lent	lent
let	let	let
lie	lay	lain
light	lit	lit
lose	lost	lost
make	made	made
mean	meant	meant
meet	met	met
must	had to	had to
pay	paid	paid
put	put	put
read	read	read
ride	rode	ridden
ring	rang	rung
rise	rose	risen
run	ran	run
say	said	said
see	saw	seen
sell	sold	sold
send	sent	sent
set	set	set
shake	shook	shaken
shine	shone	shone
shoot	shot	shot
show	showed	shown/showed
shut	shut	shut
sing	sang	sung
sit	sat	sat
sleep	slept	slept
speak	spoke	spoken
spend	spent	spent
spoil	spoilt/spoiled	spoilt/spoiled
stand	stood	stood
steal	stole	stolen
stick	stuck	stuck
swim	swam	swum
take	took	taken
teach	taught	taught
tear	tore	torn
tell	told	told
think	thought	thought
throw	threw	thrown
understand	understood	understood
wake	woke	woken
wear	wore	worn
win	won	won
write	wrote	written

Phonemic symbols

Single vowel sounds

/iː/	tree /triː/	/ə/	computer /kəmˈpjuːtə(r)/
/ɪ/	his /hɪz/	/ɜː/	learn /lɜːn/
/i/	happy /ˈhæpi/	/ɔː/	four /fɔː(r)/
/ʊ/	good /gʊd/	/æ/	hat /hæt/
/u/	usual /ˈjuːʒuəl/	/ʌ/	sunny /ˈsʌni/
/uː/	school /skuːl/	/ɑː/	car /kɑː(r)/
/e/	ten /ten/	/ɒ/	clock /klɒk/

Diphthongs (double vowel sounds)

/ɪə/	near /nɪə(r)/	/ɔɪ/	boy /bɔɪ/
/ʊə/	tour /tʊə(r)/	/aɪ/	try /traɪ/
/eə/	wear /weə(r)/	/əʊ/	so /səʊ/
/eɪ/	train /treɪn/	/aʊ/	out /aʊt/

Consonant sounds

/p/	pen /pen/	/s/	see /siː/
/b/	big /bɪg/	/z/	lazy /ˈleɪzi/
/t/	tea /tiː/	/ʃ/	shower /ˈʃaʊə(r)/
/d/	do /duː/	/ʒ/	television /ˈtelɪvɪʒn/
/tʃ/	children /ˈtʃɪldrən/	/m/	man /mæn/
/dʒ/	journey /ˈdʒɜːni/	/n/	never /ˈnevə(r)/
/k/	cat /kæt/	/ŋ/	sing /sɪŋ/
/g/	go /gəʊ/	/h/	hot /hɒt/
/f/	fly /flaɪ/	/l/	like /laɪk/
/v/	very /ˈveri/	/r/	river /ˈrɪvə(r)/
/θ/	thing /θɪŋ/	/w/	water /ˈwɔːtə(r)/
/ð/	this /ðɪs/	/j/	yes /jes/

ACKNOWLEDGEMENTS

Cover photograph reproduced with permission from: Getty Images/teekid.

The publisher would like to thank the following for permission to reproduce photographs:
Alamy Images pp.24 (Irish ferry/The Photolibrary Wales), 28 (platform bed/
Elizabeth Whiting & Associates), 30 (Humanitarian architecture exhibit/
Efrain Padro), 44 (George Mallory and Andrew Irvine climbing Everest/
Pictorial Press Ltd), 58 (collecting seaweed/christopher jones), 58 (picking
mushrooms/hugh nutt), 58 (allotment garden/Andrea Jones), 75 (Dillinger
wanted poster/Lordprice Collection); Bridgeman Images pp.16 (A View of
Charleston, South Carolina (oil on canvas), Mellish, Thomas (18th century)/
Ferens Art Gallery, Hull Museums, UK), 60 (Portrait of Isaac Newton (1642–
1727) 1702 (oil on canvas), Kneller, Sir Godfrey (1646–1723)/National Portrait
Gallery, London, UK), 60 (Portrait of Michael Faraday (1791–1867) 1841–42 (oil
on canvas), Phillips, Thomas (1770–1845)/National Portrait Gallery, London,
UK), 60 (Rutherford, Ernest (Nelson, New Zealand ,1871–Cambridge, 1937).
English physicist/Photo © Tarker), 62 (Las Meninas or The Family of Philip
IV, c.1656 (oil on canvas), Velazquez, Diego Rodriguez de Silva y (1599–1660)/
Prado, Madrid, Spain), 63 (The Fighting Temeraire, 1839 (oil on canvas),
Turner, Joseph Mallord William (1775–1851)/National Gallery, London,
UK), 63 (The Salone dei Cinquecento, c.1495 (photo), Simone del Pollaiuo
(Il Cronaca) (1454–1508)/Palazzo Vecchio (Palazzo della Signoria) Florence,
Italy); Corbis pp.26 (Wulingyuan scenic area/Bruno Morandi), 46 (Google
presidents relaxing at work/Catherine Karnow), 49 (Peter Higgs/Toby
Melville/Reuters), 50 (Thomas Edison/Bettmann), 55 (woman in wheelchair
with healthcare worker/iconics/a.collectionRF/amanaimages), 58 (Freegans
Community in New York/Alex Masi), 58 (picking blackberries/Marsh, Alan/
the food passionates), 61 (man looking in car mirror/Flint), 86 (man putting
cut grass in wheelchair/Zak Kendal/cultura), 86 (white sheets on clothes line/
Ron Erwin/All Canada Photos); Fight for Peace p.69 (Joseph Kamau); Getty
Images pp.4 (woman using laptop on sofa/Paul Bradbury), 5 (friends in coffee
shop/ML Harris), 6 (clocks on market stall/Alex Segre), 10 (safari in Kenya/
Visions of America), 10 (firefighter/ML Harris), 12 (film star Orson Welles/
Ernest Bachrach), 13 (picking spaghetti/Keystone), 18 (Winston Churchill/
IWM), 19 (Soichiro Honda talks with engineers/Takeyoshi Tanuma),
20 (Football coach Louis Van Gaal/ChinaFotoPress), 20 (Pep Guardiola/Christof
Stache), 30 (Pompidou centre, France/Guiziou Franck), 48 (Maya Angelou/
Stephen Chernin), 53 (French Buddhist monk and writer Matthieu Ricard/
AFP), 57 (motivational speaker concept/DrAfter123), 68 (women's football
final, 2012 Olympic Games/Khaled Desouki), 70 (cricket game/VisitBritain),
72 (Nelson and Winnie Mandela/Alexander Joe), 74 (policewoman handcuffing
man/Hill Street Studios), 78 (house attic/David Seed Photography); Kobal
Collection pp.32 (Shakespeare in Love/Miramax Films/Universal Pictures),
32 (Ocean's Eleven/Warner Bros/Marshak, Bob), 33 (The Great Beauty/Indigo
Film/Medusa Film/Babe Film/Canal+), 35 (Fantastic Four/20th Century Fox/
Hayes, Kerry), 37 (The Amazing Spiderman/Columbia Pictures); Mary Evans
Picture Library pp.44 (1922 British Mount Everest expedition), 54 (free school

run under a metro bridge, India/Altaf Qadri/AP); North News and Pictures
Ltd p.66 (Nick Bell/Paul Kingston/NorthNews); Ossur p.39 (artificial knee);
Oxford University Press pp.16 (*Kidnapped* book cover), 20 (football match/
Score by Aflo), 26 (seven sisters white chalk cliffs/Image Source), 41 (hurricane
satellite image/Purestock), 44 (*The Everest Story* book cover), 72 (*Nelson Mandela*
book cover); Rex Features pp.30 (Transitional Cathedral, Christchurch/View
Pictures), 69 (Paralympic World Cup Basketball/Andrew Schofield), 77 (Ashley
Olsen/Buzz Foto), 84 (Joseph Nye/Roger@RogerAskePhotography.co.uk);
Shutterstock pp.10 (worker cleaning windows/FrameAngel), 11 (lightning
over beach/Netfalls – Remy Musser), 15 (patient in ambulance/Tyler Olson),
21 (office meeting/Monkey Business Images), 22 (businesswoman in office/
Edhar), 23 (two shipping boxes/Quang Ho), 23 (aluminium foil/Sergiy Kuzmin),
23 (stack of newspapers/qvist), 23 (green lighter/Piyaphat Detbun), 23 (glass
plate award/rangizzzz), 23 (roll of silver duct tape/Anteromite), 23 (black
paint can/Gulgun Ozaktas), 23 (cardboard/Africa Studio), 25 (tropical white
sand beach/Efired), 26 (black soil/Julija Sapic), 26 (boulders/superoke),
26 (mountain peaks/TTphoto), 26 (garden centre/debra millet), 26 (waterfall/
lkunl), 27 (cruising boat on rainforest river/Vitaly Titov & Maria Sidelnikova),
29 (Mo i Rana, Norway/norr), 34 (black watercolour/sleepwalker), 38 (traffic
jam/1000 Words), 38 (parked cars/gallimaufry), 40 (flooding/Lisa S.),
43 (couple in cafe/Ekaterina Pokrovsky), 47 (young man kite boarding/
EpicStockMedia), 52 (friends at the cinema/StockLite), 54 (avatar icons/
Beatriz Gascon J), 57 (woman giving speech/l i g h t p o e t), 58 (couple picking
vegetables/auremar), 71 (Dubai skyline/DDCoral), 82 (fruit cereal loops/Brent
Hofacker), 83 (handshake/Alexander Raths), 86 (young woman smelling
flowers/KonstantinChristian); The Advertising Archives pp.80 (Mars advert),
80 (Remington advert), 81 (Volkswagen advert); The Observer p.67 (Shazia
Saleem/Sophia Spring/The Observer); The Post and Courier p.11 (Barry McRoy).

*The authors and publisher are grateful to those who have given permission to reproduce
the following extracts and adaptations of copyright material:* p.16 Extract from
Oxford Bookworm Library 3: *Kidnapped* by Robert Louis Stevenson, retold
by Clare West © Oxford University Press 2008. Reproduced by permission.
p.44 Extract from Oxford Bookworms Library 3 Factfile: *The Everest Story* by
Tim Vicary © Oxford University Press 2010. Reproduced by permission. p.72
Extract from Oxford Bookworms Library 4 Factfile: *Nelson Mandela* by Rowena
Akinyemi © Oxford University Press 2008. Reproduced by permission.

Sources: www.instructables.com, www.bbc.co.uk/news, www.express.co.uk